An Introduction to
HAWAI‘I’S NATURAL HISTORY

By Wind, By Wave was produced
with the support and encouragement of the
Polynesian Voyaging Society and
Kamehameha Schools

By Wind, By Wave

An Introduction to
HAWAI'I'S NATURAL HISTORY

David L. Eyre

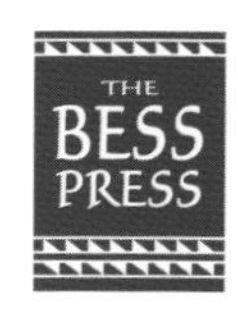

3565 Harding Ave. Honolulu, Hawai'i 96816 • Phone (808) 734-7159 • Fax (808) 732-3627
www.besspress.com

Design: Carol Colbath
Index: Lee S. Motteler

Library of Congress Cataloging-in-Publication Data

Eyre, David L.
By wind, by wave : an introduction to Hawai'i's natural history / David L. Eyre.
p. cm.
Includes illustrations, glossary, bibliography, index.
ISBN 1-57306-112-3
1. Natural history – Hawaii. I. Title.
QH198.H3.E86 1999 508.969-dc20

Printed in Korea

To my father

David W. Eyre

in gratitude for the convictions and enthusiasms

he has brought to our lives

Contents

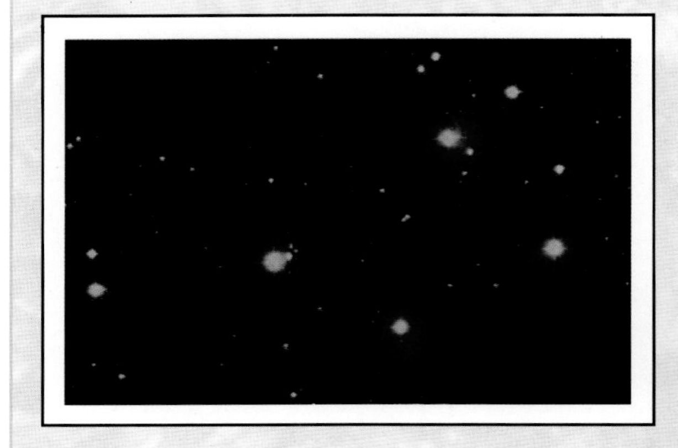

WESTERN SETTLEMENT: MANY NEW THINGS 76

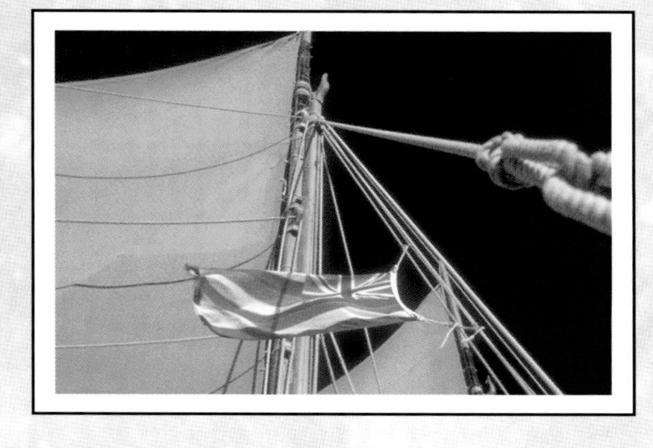

ALOHA 'ĀINA— RESPONSIBLE STEWARDSHIP: IT MATTERS GREATLY 152

Foreword

It is a huge honor for us to be asked to write a foreword to *By Wind, By Wave*, in which David Eyre shares his respect and love for Hawai'i. This is the first book on Hawai'i's natural history written for island students from an island perspective. It is much needed and will be cherished.

By Wind, By Wave has been chosen by the Polynesian Voyaging Society (PVS) to use in gift-giving because it exemplifies the Society's Mālama Hawai'i vision, which is that

Hawai'i, our special island home,
Be a place where the land and sea are cared for
And communities are healthy and safe for all people.

The Polynesian Voyaging Society's original purpose of researching the manner in which Polynesian seafarers settled Hawai'i has been successfully fulfilled, and its focus has turned to contributing to the quality of life of all Hawai'i's people by sharing that knowledge through education and community-building. *By Wind, By Wave* adds to that contribution by reaching out to young—and not-so-young—minds with fascinating information presented in a stimulating style. It puts us "in the same canoe" by using the Guiding Values of PVS:

aloha	to love
mālama	to care for
'imi 'ike	to seek knowledge
lokomaika'i	to share with each other
na'au pono	to nurture a deep sense of justice
olakino maika'i	to live healthily

It is with deep *aloha* that we welcome *By Wind, By Wave* as a major influence in helping to keep Hawai'i the special place it is, and with deep gratitude that we thank David for his fine work.

Pinky and Laura Thompson

Preface

One scientist has called Hawaiʻi "the finest natural laboratory for the study of evolution in the world," while another refers to it as "the extinction capital of the world." Both statements are equally true and suggest compelling reasons why the study of Hawaiʻi's natural history should be an educational priority. It is disturbing, therefore, that this subject receives so little attention in texts currently used in our schools or in the public debate.

The aim of this book is to introduce general themes of Hawaiʻi's natural history to younger readers—and to interested adults as well. Included in the text is a representative sampling of animals selected to exemplify these themes. In their interactions with humans and the environment, many of these animals have left their marks. Their tracks, bites, chirps, stings and droppings have been part of the experience of children growing up in this land. As such, they are also an important part of Hawaiʻi's cultural and social history.

The choice of animals charts distinct periods on a historic timeline. First, a pristine "Hawaiʻi Before Humans," where gods, green turtles, tree snails and a comparatively small number of other species inhabited the land; then, "Hawaiian Settlement" of the islands, when intentional and unintentional species introductions affected the land; and finally, the dramatic impact of "Western Settlement," with the resulting vast transformation of the land. The concluding section of the text presents examples of "*Aloha ʻĀina*–Responsible Stewardship" as inspiring models for how humans might become good stewards, safeguarding what remains of our precious Hawaiian homeland and its natural heritage.

For each animal presented, a "More Facts" section provides additional information about the animal as well as main themes of Hawaiʻi's natural history. The "Views" bring in the experience, expertise and opinions of many different people, enriching a given topic with more perspective. The "Just Wondering" passages attempt to stir a sense of wonder-filled questioning. Such questions don't necessarily lead to a tidy, textbook reply: wonder in and of itself is enough. As Albert Einstein put it so well: "The most beautiful thing we can experience is the mysterious."

This book seeks to convey a sense of how remarkable, how absolutely extraordinary these islands are. Though the Galápagos Islands received much early scientific and public attention, it is widely felt that if Charles Darwin had visited Hawaiʻi he would have been considerably more impressed with these lovely and varied islands. Hawaiʻi is now generally recognized as the more spectacular biologically, a place of fragile magic, of absolute singularity. But are we who live here aware of this? And do we care?

Hawaiʻi also has the dubious distinction of being further down the somber path of environmental destruction and species extinction than most other places. Some 70 percent of recorded extinctions in the United States during the past two hundred years are of plant and animal species found only in Hawaiʻi. Sadly, much of what has happened to Hawaiʻi's environment is beginning to occur elsewhere on our small planet. In this regard, these islands are an important indicator area: where Hawaiʻi now finds itself is an indication of where other areas very probably are headed.

Thus, what we in Hawai'i do matters greatly. Our experience is applicable to areas following closely behind us; the models we devise for saving, sustaining and restoring threatened habitats and the species they support will be available as valuable solutions for others elsewhere. Education is generally seen as the crucial prerequisite for developing such solutions.

By Wind, By Wave encourages readers both to be aware and to care. It is a call to understanding and a call to action, providing a new generation of *nā keiki o ka 'āina* a more "local" look at some aspects of the rich, complex and often painful story of Hawai'i's natural history, of this land that is rightfully theirs. For, as an African proverb puts it, "Natural areas are not given to us by our fathers but are loaned to us by our children."

E aloha 'āina kākou! Let us love the land!

Mahalo

By Wind, By Wave builds on the work and talents of many people, most important the authors and researchers who provided the information base. Specific chapters of the manuscript were submitted to the following experts for content accuracy: George H. Balazs, green turtle; Robert Cowie and Michael Hadfield, Oʻahu tree snail; Keith Unger, Hawaiian crow; Phil Bruner and Oscar W. Johnson, Pacific golden plover; Allen Allison and Dwayne Uyeda, gecko; Pascual Dabis, pig; Gordon Nishida, all insects; James Mejeur, ostrich; John Bedish, brush-tailed rock wallaby; Mike Yamamoto, tilapia. Cynthia Salley and Nainoa Thompson reviewed sections on their contributions to *aloha ʻāina*. I am indebted to these people for the knowledge they so generously shared and their enthusiastic support.

Alison Kay, devoted naturalist, teacher and writer, played a pivotal role as the project evolved. Early on, Alison provided bracing and constructive criticism, helping to focus the work to the form it has now taken. During the editing process, she stood tireless watch over the many details of science, assuring accuracy and precision. Her exacting spirit is everywhere felt.

Kēhau Cachola-Abad, Henry Bennett, David Boynton, Kahikina de Silva, Betsy Gagné, Charlene Hoe, Liana Honda, Clemi McLaren, Dick Mills, Anita Manning, Steve Montgomery, Larry Morden and Sylvia Wilmeth reviewed the manuscript and provided many valuable suggestions.

Eliza Jewett looked at the text with the eyes and brightness of a very informed younger reader and offered many cogent suggestions.

Sigrid Southworth, head of the Hawaiian Collection at Midkiff Learning Center, Kamehameha Schools, devoted boundless energy and great enthusiasm to helping this project in essential ways.

My sincere thanks also to the following:

Chris and Sally Aall, Melanie Adams, Mike Chun, Neil Hannahs, Tommy Higashino, ʻAnela Iaea, Bill Mull, Kathy Kukea, Keʻala Kwan, Chonita and Jack Larsen, Bruce Lum, Laura Robinson, Keola Wong, Mimi Wong, Elisa Yadao, Janet Zisk, and The Nature Conservancy of Hawaiʻi, who have supported *By Wind, By Wave* with their time, encouragement and aloha.

My students and fellow teachers at Kamehameha, who with such gracious patience have seen their *kumu* and colleague through the task of writing this book.

The Bess Press staff—Publisher Buddy Bess, Editor Revé Shapard and Art Director Carol Colbath—for the competent, caring and respectful approach they have brought to the process of creating a book.

I am indebted to my family for helping to make this book possible: my wife Cathy Hōkūlani for being there in every way; my children Sintra, Lisa, Emma, Makana, and Alea for their patience when "daddy-work" got in the way; my uncle Ralph Cake who provided me friendship, a simple desk and a spare room in which to write; Walbert and Ethel Chong for their continued support; and my father, David W. Eyre, who keeps things going joyously for all of us.

The mistakes that may remain, despite the best efforts of these many good and talented people, are mine alone.

Photo Credits

A generous grant by Kamehameha Schools made possible the acquisition of many of the photos used in this book. It is with much *aloha* that I acknowledge the support of my school and the legacy of Princess Bernice Pauahi Bishop in nurturing the education of Hawai'i's children in the area of *mālama 'āina.*

Lead photographer David Boynton's beautiful pictures establish the visual tone of *By Wind, By Wave* from the very start. A devoted teacher and environmentalist, David wholeheartedly supported the notion that Hawai'i's teens deserve as good a book on natural history as we could muster. His contribution is an essential part of this work and he has my sincere *aloha* and gratitude. David provided the following photos: front cover, back cover flap, v, vii(l), xi, 1, 2t, 2b, 3, 5, 6, 7, 8t, 8b, 9l, 9r, 10, 11, 12, 13, 14, 24, 29, 30br, 31t, 37, 41, 44, 47t, 48, 49t, 49b, 51t, 51b, 52t, 52b, 54, 55, 57tl, 57tr, 58, 60b, 63b, 64, 65, 66b, 67t, 67b, 68r, 69t, 70, 75bl, 84tl, 85t, 87bl, 89, 92bl, 96t, 97b, 98tr, 104tl, 108, 112ml, 112bl, 118t, 120, 128t, 131, 132, 133, 135, 136bl, 137, 143b, 146l, 147, 148t, 148b, 153, 155tl.

Significant visual contributions were made by

Monte Costa, photographer for the Polynesian Voyaging Society, vi(r), vii(r), 17, 50, 73t, 73b, 152br, 155br, 160, 161, 162 and

Dennis Kunkel, University of Hawai'i, 86b, 87br, 88tr, 88bl, 90br, 91, 92tl, 92ml, 96b, 97t, 97m, 98tl, 101, 102, 113br, 123t, 140b

In addition, the following people opened their hearts and files to this project, sharing generously to make pages come alive visually:

Allen Allison, 66t, 68t, 136tr
George H. Balazs, back cover (top), 16t, 16b, 19, 20, 21t, 21b
A.J.Berger, 84tr (courtesy of Betsy Gagné)
Pascual Dabis, 72
David L. Eyre, 109t, 109b, 122, 123b
Betsy Gagné, xi, 13, 30tl, 38t, 38b, 68b, 71t, 71b, 75br, 128b, 138b, 154, 155tr
Wayne Gagné, 152tl (courtesy of Betsy Gagné)
Michael Hadfield, back cover (bottom), 25, 26tl, 26bl, 27t, 28bl, 31b, 32b
Chris Johns, 90tl
Oscar W. Johnson, 42, 43, 45t, 45b, 46t, 46b, 47b
Charles Lamoureux, 155bl
Bianca Lavies, 115
Anita Manning, 119bl
Steve Montgomery, 30bl, 32t, 103t, 103br, 105, 114t, 114bl, 114br, 117
Bill Mull, 27b, 90bl, 94l, 94r, 102, 141
Gordon Nishida, 86t, 92br, 112tl, 113tr, 119tr, 121r, 121bl, 138t, 139, 143t
Lynn M. Rosenblatt, 98bl, 98br, 99tr, 99br, 99bl, 100tl, 100tr, 100bl
Michael T. Sipe, tilapia geneticist, 149t
Keith Unger, 156t, 156b
Michael Walther, 130

A number of institutions also provided material:

Bishop Museum, 106
Hawai'i Humane Society, 63t
Hawai'i State Archives, 28tr, 28br, 53, 56t, 56b, 57b, 60t, 69b, 76, 77l, 77r, 78, 79, 80, 81t, 81b, 82, 83t, 83b, 85b, 104br, 107, 118ml, 118bl
Honolulu Zoo, 59, 61

Mission Houses Museum, 62, 95
NASA, vi(l), 4
State of Hawai'i
Department of Agriculture/ Aquaculture Development Program, 144t, 144b, 145, 146t, 149b, 151tl, 151bl, 151tr, 151br
Department of Land and Natural Resources/Division of Aquatic Resources, 152bl
Division of Forestry and Wildlife
Jon Giffin, 111
Cyndi Kuehler, the Peregrine Fund, 146b, 152tr, 157, 158tl, 158tr, 158br, 159bl, 159br
S. Robinson, 126 & 127t
Bill Stormont, 124tl, 124br, 125
Ron Walker, 127b, 129
U.S. Fish and Wildlife Service, 39t, 39b, 40
Paul Banko, back cover (middle), 34t, 35t, 35b, 36t, 36tl
Peter Harrity, the Peregrine Fund, 34b
JK, the Peregrine Fund, 26tr, 33
M. Lusk, 23b
Craig Rowland, 18, 23t
R.J. Shallenberger, 36b
Van Waters & Rogers Inc., 87tr, 87mr, 142

Hawai'i Before Humans: Beautiful and Curious Works of Creation

Beginnings: Ocean Eruptions

The surface of the Earth is a thin, cool crust covering a hot interior globe of molten rock. This crust is cracked into great slab-like sections called tectonic plates. Geologists count a dozen major plates as well as many lesser ones that puzzle together the surface of our planet. These plates lie on top of the Earth's mantle, a layer of semisolid rock material called magma. They are not stationary but in slight movement, shifting ever so slowly and creating tremendous force as they move against each other. At certain weak spots in these plates, magma pushes up through the crust and erupts as a volcano.

It was at just such a weak spot in the depths of the central north Pacific that the history of Hawai'i began some one hundred million years ago. Geologists call this creation source of our islands the Hawaiian hot spot.

Running up from the deep molten belly of the Earth, lava ruptured from a sea floor crack nearly three miles below the

Fiery magma floods seaward.

ocean's surface. For hundreds of thousands of years the undersea volcano pushed up: erupting magma heaved higher and higher, piling up layer upon layer of lava, toward the far-off stained-glass light of the swells above. At last, this crusty rubble pile—the scalding summit of a massive underwater mountain—smoldered through the ocean's surface. An island was born.

Black and lifeless in a boundless expanse of blue sea and bluer sky, this island was the beginning of our Hawaiʻi.

The Hawaiian Islands were created one after another in assembly-line fashion at this single volcanic source. As the Hawaiian hot spot has issued repeated eruptions, the Pacific Plate has slid northward, slowly carrying its immense mountains away to the northwest at a speed of about three inches a year.

And as each new volcano in its time gradually moved away from the stationary source of lava, a new eruption began to build behind it. Many volcanoes never reached the ocean surface: the sea floor along our chain is pimpled with hundreds of cones that cooled and went dead without rising up to wind and wave.

But many underwater volcanoes did rise to become islands, and no sooner had they appeared than those forces that soon would bring them life—the rains, the winds, the waves—also began to wear away at them, slowly, slowly eroding them back down into the sea.

The older islands aged and weathered in the west, while younger islands were born and pushed up to the southeast and were in their turn carried away from the Hawaiian hot spot. It is the last born of these islands that today form the main Hawaiian chain, our homeland.

And we are still part of this ancient story. The work of creation goes on: the

The immense Pacific

The force of molten lava is seen in this pāhoehoe *lava field, Big Island of Hawai'i.*

Hawaiian hot spot presses out lava, pushes up land; active vents on the Big Island of Hawai'i spew out new outcroppings of rugged lava while to the southeast, the newly discovered infant island Lō'ihi swells up from deep beneath the sea.

The massive, colossal shifting of tectonic plates explains the separation of North America from Europe, Africa from South America, and the migration of the smaller plate of India northward until it pushed into the Asian subcontinent, the force of which shoved up the great Himalayan range. Plate drift also explains the shaking of the land near such places as San Francisco, where two great slabs grind sideways against each other along the San Andreas Fault. The huge tension of this slow grinding causes frequent quakes and tremors, some highly destructive of human communities.

The forces of nature move at very different and unpredictable speeds. Compare the sluggish drift of tectonic plates at three inches a year, the slide of a huge Alaskan glacier at 2.5 inches a day, and the sudden explosive blowout of a volcano after years, sometimes centuries, of slumber.

Just Wondering

Put down this book and hold up your fingers. The Hawaiian Islands are moving up across the Pacific Ocean at about the same speed that your fingernails are growing. Can you very quietly let that thought fill your mind's eye?

The incredible—and deadly—creative power of a volcano was related by a witness of the 1868 eruption of Mauna Loa. Here are some excerpts translated from one of the Hawaiian newspapers of the day. The author is from Ka'ū on the island of Hawai'i.

The Hawaiian Islands and the encircling sea, as photographed from the space shuttle

Views

"On the 27th of March we saw Mauna Loa standing peacefully there, with not a sign of a cloud. Only a few minutes after that, we saw a column of smoke rise like a cloud. Soon after that the cloud reddened on the summit of Mauna Loa and a stream of lava turned westward and rushed like a running stream.

The earthquakes were terrible from the 27th to the 30th. The earth shook constantly. We had never before known anything like this. The stones on our beaches and cliffs are scattered and broken. . . .

We also heard that a whaling ship, passing Hawai'i, was tossed up and down while cliffsides slid down into the sea. . . . At 3 o'clock on Thursday, April 2, came a great quake which made it impossible for men and animals to stand upright . . . big trees toppled over; gulches were filled with houses collapsed. . . . Fifteen minutes after the earthquake, a tidal wave arose which killed a number of people. Those who died numbered 46, and those who barely escaped with their lives are not numbered. Some corpses were recovered and some were not, as the sea had swept them away. . . . When the sea ebbed all kinds of fish were left ashore, except the whale and the shark.

The height attained by the rising tide was equal to that of the coconut trees that grew near those houses. This tidal wave was unlike any other seen in these islands. It was a very peculiar one . . . it was a sea that swirled upward."

(C.J. Waialoha, Ka Nūpepa Kū'oko'a, *April 11-18, 1868, trans. M.K. Pukui, from Handy & Handy)*

Vast Stretches of Time

To grasp the scope of geological processes, we must think big. We must comprehend that colossal pieces of the Earth's surface—even a slab as gigantic as a whole continent or the Pacific Plate—can slowly move. We must also try to grasp vast stretches of time. A geological timeline of the formation of the Hawaiian Islands gives us a sense of the wondrous lengths of time we have to consider. The islets and atolls to the far northwest of the Hawaiian chain are as old as seventy million years. Kaua'i and O'ahu are some four to five million years old, while the island of Hawai'i is the youngest island at about five hundred thousand to seven hundred thousand years old—a mere moment on the geological timeline. As noted above, the next island to well up from the Hawaiian hot spot has been named Lōʻihi. Now a half mile beneath the surface, it is scheduled to make its appearance in the blink of a geological eye—some ten thousand to twenty thousand years from now.

Just Wondering

How do we grasp quantities that are of cosmic proportions—say, the size of the galaxy that surrounds us? The universe contains as many as 100 billion great swirls of stars, called galaxies. Clustered in each galaxy are as many as 100 billion stars. In the galaxy called the Milky Way is a star we call the sun. Orbiting the sun like a blue marble is our planet—a planet of cloud and soil and sea. As we lie on our backs on a Hawaiian beach and gaze at the glistening haze of stars above, do our senses go numb at the vastness of the universe?

Isolation: The Vast Encircling Sea

The Hawaiian Islands are the most geographically isolated archipelago in the world, dotting the ocean some twenty-two hundred miles from the nearest continent. The sea that surrounds us is huge beyond our imaginations. To get some sense of the immensity of this area, we could cut up a map of Europe, Asia, Africa, Australia, all of North and South America, and piece it together in the Pacific Ocean with space to spare. When measured from the ocean bottom, Mauna Loa looms as the largest single mountain on Earth, but, seen from a satellite, it is only a speck on this vast expanse of ocean. In depth as well, the Pacific is awe-inspiring, dropping down some three miles in cold darkness. Here is a description of the Pacific Ocean by a scientist who spent many years studying this vast encircling sea:

The evening sea heaves rhythmically as huge swells ripple to shore.

Views

"The Pacific Ocean is a huge affair: it is long and wide and deep. From Bering Sea to Wilkes Land on the Antarctic Circle the distance is 9,300 miles, and along the equator the distance is 10,000 miles—two-fifths of the circumference of the earth—and more than three times the width of the Atlantic. These great stretches of water form the axis of an area comprising more than 55,000,000 square miles—the area of the United States is about 3,000,000 square miles. The Pacific is nearly twice the size of the Atlantic and greater in area than all the continents and islands combined. The volume of Pacific water is incomprehensibly great. If all the lands above sea level—plains, plateaus, and mountain systems—were piled into the Pacific they would sink to the bottom and be submerged at a depth of about 12,000 feet. If the water were drained from the Pacific the descent from the present shore line to the floor of the deepest valley would be greater than the present ascent to the loftiest Himalayan peak."

(H.E. Gregory, Director, Bishop Museum, 1928)

More than any other factor, it is the isolation of these islands in this great salty expanse that has shaped Hawai'i's natural history. All plant and animal life had to come from somewhere else, drifting in by chance across huge stretches of open ocean to what at first were specks of lifeless land. Now and then, blown by wind or borne by wave, perhaps once every hundred thousand years, a single new species made its way across the surrounding sea and established a population of its kind: a spore, a seed, a snail, a hawk, a crow. And because of Hawai'i's great isolation and the amazing variety of habitats that slowly evolved in these islands, once here, an arriving species in time changed in its own unique ways.

Just Wondering

More than two-thirds of our planet is covered with water. When seen from space, it is blue and shimmering. Why, then, do we call our planet "Earth?"

Rain: Sea to Sea

The immense stretches of open sea surrounding Hawai'i have had a moderating and stabilizing effect on the climate of these islands. Winds reaching the bare land first sweep across thousands of miles of open water, gathering up moisture as they blow. Meeting Hawai'i's steep volcanic flanks, the breezes rise up and cool. Because cold air is less capable of holding water, the moisture the breezes carry forms clouds, which then release their rain. In time, the water trickles and tumbles its way down rocky mountain streams, threading its way back to the sea.

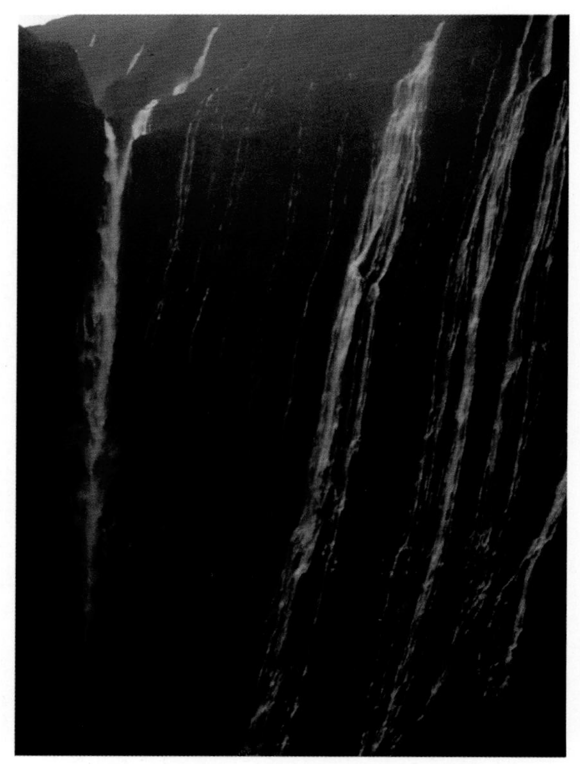

A drenching Kaua'i rain rushes back to the ocean.

Kaua'i ridges, sliced thin and steep by mountain streams

»»»»»» *Just Wondering* »»»»»»

The voyage of water from sea to cloud to stream and back to sea is described here in very simple terms. Actually, the way of water through the world is a marvelously powerful and complex process known as the water cycle. What's more, it is an ancient voyage: most of the water on Earth is some four billion years old. Clouds and streams and rivers are major transporters of water. At any given time, much of the world's water (about 97 percent) is found in its seas and oceans. But there are many other places where "Earth's blood" is held for longer or shorter periods as it makes its way on its cycle. What are some of these places? Where do we go for a glass of "fresh" water?

SOIL: WASHED ASH

Billowing dust and thick ash spewing from a volcanic eruption begin the process of soil formation on the new island. Rain washes the dust and ash to muddy thickness. Later, when plants appear, drop their leaves and fruit, then die and decay, their organic material in the form of humus helps to build up a rich soil, slowly making the land more welcoming to a seed or spore or bug that may blow in.

EROSION: AN ISLAND RETURNS TO THE SEA

From the start, opposing forces of creation and destruction are at work on a new island, for no sooner has land risen up from the sea than wind and rain and wave begin to wear and break it back down—slowly, relentlessly—over thousands of years.

Because of the northwesterly drift of the Pacific Plate, the islands of the Hawaiian chain are progressively older as one moves from Hawai'i to Maui, Maui to O'ahu and onward past Kaua'i and

Ni'ihau to the highly eroded coral reefs of Kure, an atoll some sixteen hundred miles away. Similarly, within each island, the eastern mountains are younger than those to the west. On Maui, for example, Haleakalā, in the east, is comparatively young, while at the west end of the island, Pu'u Kukui is more deeply wrinkled by the rub of erosion. On O'ahu, the Ko'olau Mountains are younger than the western Wai'anae Range, which—in a few million years perhaps—will be the first of the two ranges reclaimed by the sea.

As humans living in the brief time of now, we can glimpse this patient work in progress—in the surf-carved cliffs, the reddish wash of rainy soil staining a stormy sea, and the wind made visible by the dust it sweeps off, or perhaps as we bravely paddle down Waikīkī's smelly, sludge-clogged Ala Wai Canal. It is estimated that about half the original land mass of the island of O'ahu is already gone—carried away by erosion. Even the youthful Mauna Loa, at 13,796 feet the largest single mountain on Earth, will one day be washed and worn and rubbed into the sea. These islands will eventually slump back down to the great sea cradle from which they first emerged.

Colonization: Life Comes to Lava

By Wind

How then did life come to lava? When a flow of lava has cooled and stiffened, life comes quickly to the raw rock. Early traces of green on a recent flow suggest how the first life forms may have once been established on a bare new island. Within a year, dustlike plant spores arrive with the wind. If there is rain, algae, mosses, and ferns are soon seen greening the

Lichen whitens lava.

stark, dark rock. Lichens sprout by the third year and seed plants in the fourth. Seeds of the *'ōhi'a lehua* are tiny (two will tuck into the top space of the letter "e") and easily blown great distances to new areas. These plants can all grow directly on lava well before the formation of soil.

Animals also make their way quickly

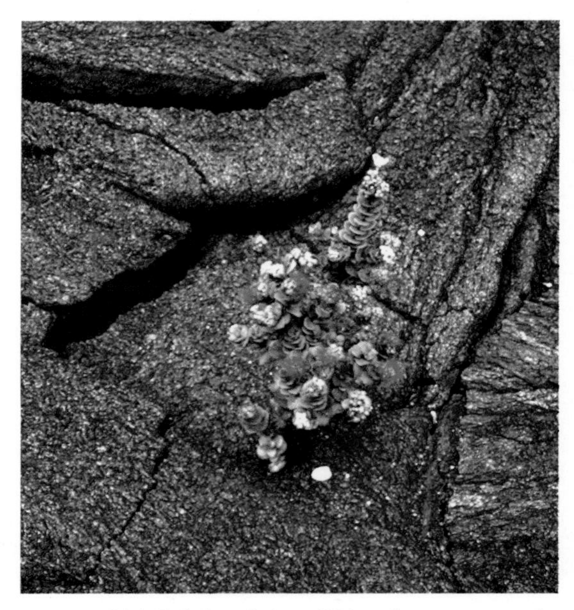

Stumped 'ōhi'a lehua *brings life's colors to raw rock.*

to new outcroppings of lava. In the early 1970s, a black, big-eyed cricket was discovered on a flow of lava where no life was then known. The discovery came within a month of eruption. These crickets feed on tiny, windblown organic debris and seem to play a role in helping to make the new environment more welcoming to colonizing plants.

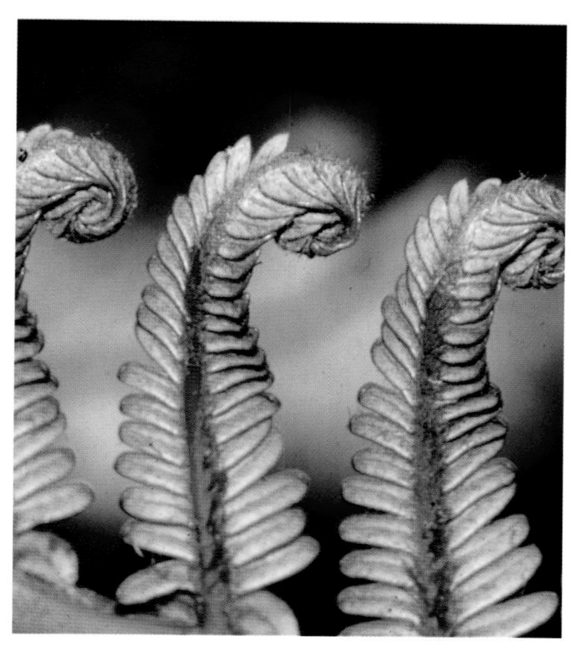

Endemic ʻamaʻu *fern (detail)*

Scientists call the first plants and animals to arrive "colonizers," for they were the species that established the first colonies of life on this land. Only a very few species are thought to have succeeded in crossing the vast salty barrier that separates Hawaiʻi from other lands. It is estimated that about 275 plant species, 250 insect species, 25 snail species, and 15 bird species were among the founding colonizers of life on these islands as we know it today.

Just as *ʻōhiʻa* seeds are blown to newly hardened lava, where they take root and grow, so too were spores and seeds of other plants blown by chance over the Pacific, settling on a newly created island. Over 150 different kinds of ferns now grow in Hawaiʻi. The tiny colonizing spores of these species probably all drifted in, lifted along by wind, over many millions of years. Lightweight insects are easily blown great distances as well. A Bishop Museum scientist demonstrated this by setting up large trap nets on a ship far from the nearest island. Numerous insects were snagged as they sifted by, wind-borne on currents of air. In another experiment, nets were attached to the air intakes of a plane, which then flew thousands of feet above the ocean. When the plane landed, dead insects, spiders and even tiny pebbles were emptied from the traps. The salty winds it seems, even at very high altitudes, are dotted with floating insects.

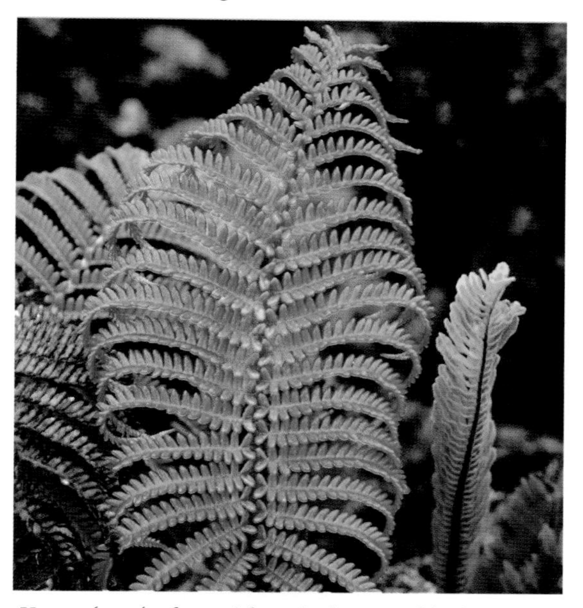

Young ʻamaʻu *fern with typical orange blush*

Seeds with hooks, sticky surfaces, barbs or bristly hairs cling to a bird's feathers just as they clasp to our cuffs when we walk through a field of high grass. More than twenty kinds of ducks and geese, as well as many other far-wandering species of birds, regularly pass through the islands on their yearly migrations. Today, some one thousand migrating ducks stop over in Hawai'i every year, far fewer than in the 1950s, when about ten thousand duck arrivals were counted annually. These big birds belonging to other lands have probably made visits to ocean islands since the beginning of time. (In 1943, a flock of ducks set down on Palmyra Island, located a thousand miles to the south of Honolulu. Several of the ducks wore tags indicating they had come from Utah.) On arrival, the birds preen themselves, combing out the seeds onto the ground. Seeds and tiny snails also probably came to Hawai'i stuck in dried mud smeared on a duck's webbed foot.

Birds carry seeds in their intestines as well, leftovers from a final supper on the shore of departure. A bird in flight can hold its stomach contents up to 120 hours, ample time to fly with the wind to a distant destination. Snails, a food for some of these birds, are particularly stout voyagers, their shell and slime seal shutting them into their capsules like hard little pills. One scientist recorded opening the body of a pigeon that had been dead for three days and finding thirteen tiny snails. He placed them in a saucer of water and they soon slid out of their tight chambers.

By Wave

Early colonizers quite likely floated their way to these new islands as well. A few creatures may have hitched a ride on logs or organic debris that frequently collects to form large mats. The floating mats—pushed by wind, prodded by waves—eventually wash up on distant beaches. Yearly storms in the Pacific Northwest tear trees off cliffs, sending them crashing into the ocean to float off on the high sea, some eventually to roll ashore on Pacific islands. Insects tucked beneath bark and sufficiently sheltered from the killing salt sea occasionally may have survived such long voyages:

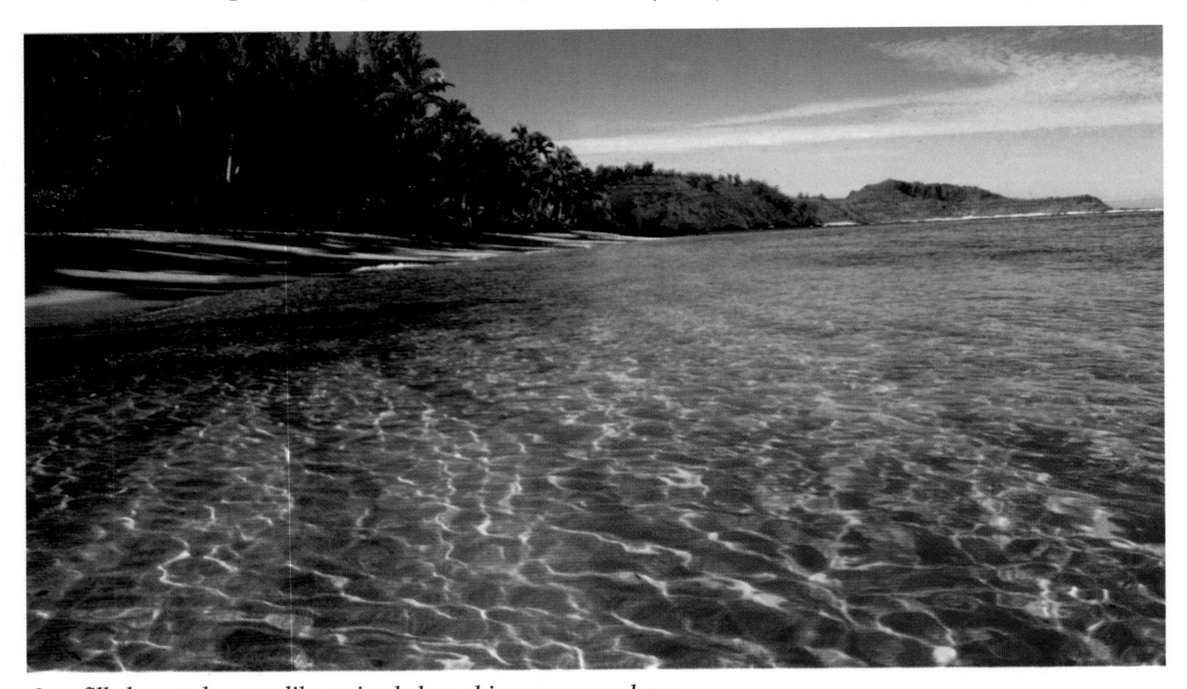

Sun-filled coastal water, like stained glass, shimmers near shore.

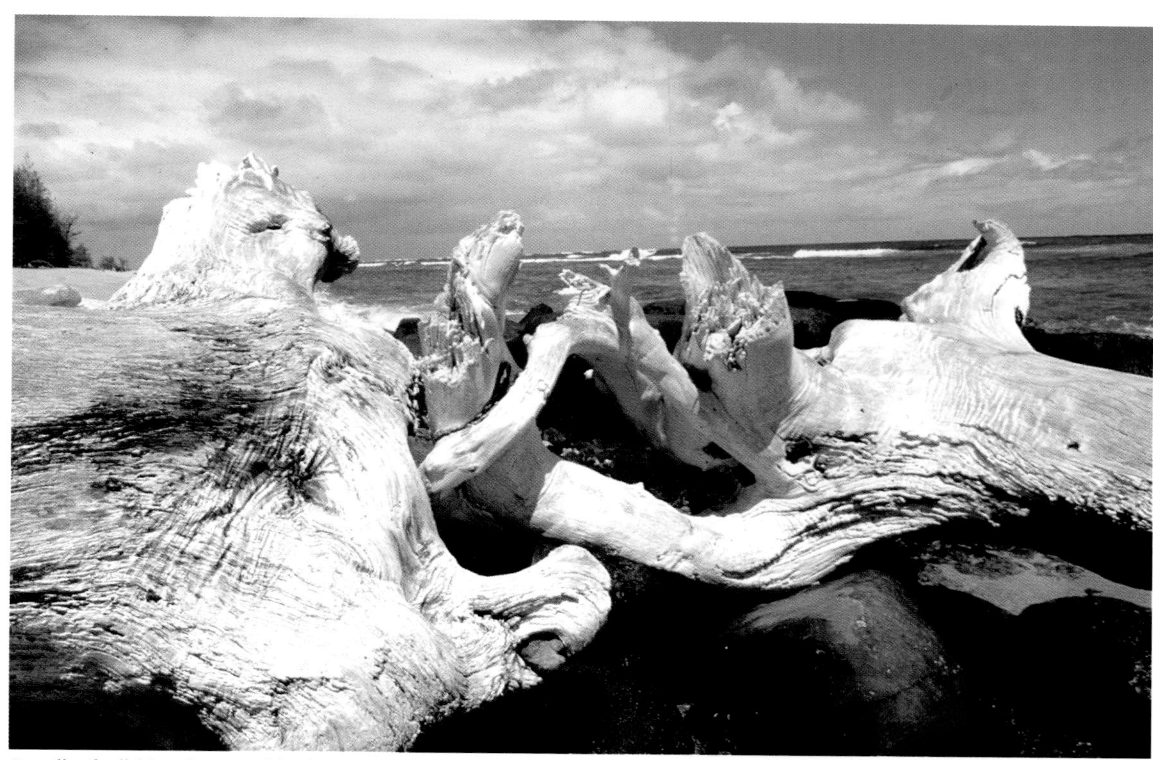

Log "rafts," like these, rubbed raw and white by the elements, may have carried seeds or small creatures to colonize the islands of Hawai'i.

Views

"I have seen large trees washed from stream sides during a storm in Tahiti and have seen them floating out to sea with their large branches riding high out of the water. The large, heavy trunks, great root masses in which are entangled stones and soil, and the submerged limbs may act as keel, ballast and stabilizers and hold a part of such floating trees permanently out of the water. Some of the branches may be held 20 or more feet above the waves. At rare intervals, colonies of animals and seeds may be able to survive lengthy journeys in such perches. It is conceivable that over a period of several millions of years a few such floating trees have been beached in Hawai'i and that from them there escaped ancestors of some of our insects, terrestrial mollusks and plants."

(E. C. Zimmerman, 1948)

Scientists use the term "rafting" to describe the drifting, on a tree or other debris, of a plant or animal that may eventually colonize new land. Seeds are known to float great distances, their tough skins protecting them from the salt. The coconut, for example, with its corky, buoyant husk, floats like a glass ball and easily drifted from island to island throughout Polynesia, later to be introduced to Hawai'i on the first voyaging canoes. Seeds of the *naupaka*, which is a common shoreline species in Hawai'i, probably bobbed their way to these islands. Flung by a storm wave above the high-tide line, a few would sprout and root quickly into new lives on these beaches. Where the sand meets the land, a lushness grew.

Though we cannot know for sure how individual plants and animals made their

Amidst the mist, towering ‘ōhi‘a lehua *seem to dissolve in the dusk.*

way to Hawai‘i and exactly where they originated, genetic technology is bringing us new and exciting information about the ancient origins of Hawaiian species. Scientists have established, for example, that most native Hawaiian species trace their origins to the Indo-Malaysian region of Southeast Asia and probably made their way to Hawai‘i by island-hopping across the South Pacific.

Island-hopping occurred as well within the Hawaiian archipelago as a bare new island became available for colonists from nearby older islands in the west. Not surprisingly, given that there is no landmass between Hawai‘i and North and Central America, few endemic Hawaiian species trace their origins to these places. Seventy-one percent of Hawai‘i's plants are of tropical origin, 19 percent of temperate and 10 percent of unknown origin. Ninety-five percent of Hawai‘i's native insects are traceable to Pacific sources, while only 5 percent are considered to be of American origin.

Just Wondering

"Should it come as a surprise that dandelions and flies have managed long-distance dispersal and oaks and elephants have not?"

(S. Carlquist, 1980)

Found Nowhere Else: Evolution, Speciation and Adaptive Radiation

Eventually, through a remarkable process of evolutionary give-and-take, the wind-borne, wave-borne colonizers changed the remote island world they entered—and are ever changed by it.

Long, long before the first humans chanced upon these far-off, fragile islands, the land itself rose from the sea, unique in an amazing variety of natural environments, from simmering seashore to frozen summit. Perhaps nowhere in the world is such a variety of habitats found in so small a land area. Sun-baked, bone-dry beaches ribbon Hawai‘i's leeward coasts; a few miles away, bald cinder cones, capped with glistening snow in winter, top the highest mountains. Between sea and mountain stretch wind-shaped dunes, hot lowland plains and black beds of barren lava. Damp valleys cut the land to mountain summit, draining dense, rain-drenched heights where as much as a foot of water falls a week, making them among the rainiest places on Earth. Each colonizer coming to these islands shapes—and is shaped by—the environment in which it settles.

Scientists count as many as 150 different environments—from spring-fed pool to swirling stream, from dark lava tube to icy mountain crest. In each, specialized ecosystems have evolved with unique life forms.

Just Wondering

The sun is shining on cinder cone ice and seashore sand. Why, with the same sun shining on both places, is there such temperature variation?

These habitats formed gradually over millions of years, creating a complex, fragile and fine-tuned world. When, on occasion, a colonizer arrived and settled, its descendants found themselves in this great variety of environments and came to use them differently. With the passing of time, they were themselves changed in form and structure.

No two organisms are exactly alike. Individual differences or variations are inherited. Animals and plants are also known to change with time: offspring do not look exactly like their parents. When these differences occur over several generations, or, perhaps over thousands of years, they are recognized as the result of a process known as evolution—a word that means "to unroll or unfold."

It was Charles Darwin who, after observing species on the Galápagos Islands, suggested that evolution—changes in species over time—is itself the result of a process, one he called "natural selection."

The animals and plants that colonized the Hawaiian Islands arrived in a land where environments are very different from those of their place of origin. Hawai'i is also a land of constant change. Lava spills forth, cools and ages. Soil forms on what has been black, barren rock and is gradually changed by newly arriving plants and animals. Mountains erode, and subtle changes take place in climate as trees cover valley floor and mountain slope. Colonizing species also change: only some of the offspring, differing perhaps merely slightly from their parents, survive the demands of these new and changing environments.

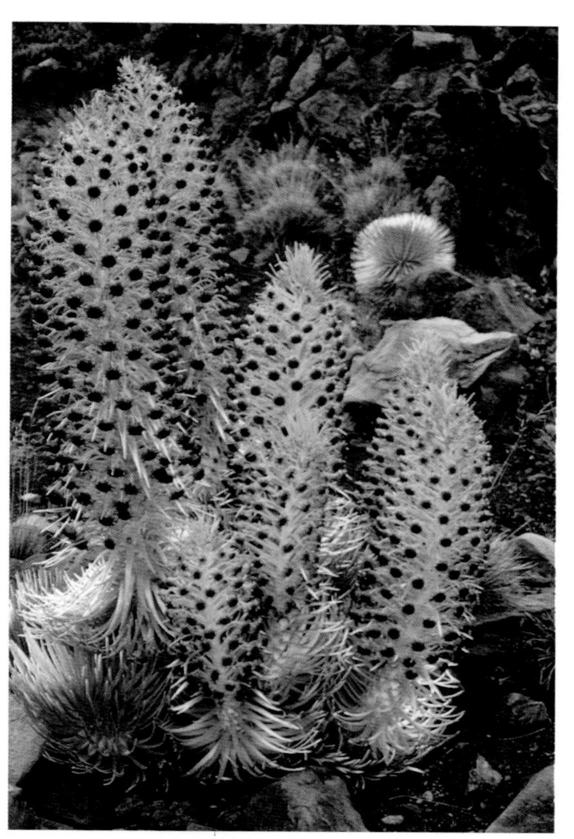

Maui greenswords rise in a rare bloom.

Thus when a few geese with large webbed feet, originally from a water world in North America, settled on crumbly dry lava in Hawai'i, offspring with the least webbing were those that survived. They had a selective advantage over the others. Today, they are the *nēnē*, our state bird.

Similar changes take place in plants. The ancestor of the majestic silversword

Endemic ʻiʻiwi; *its bill mirrors native lobelia flowers.*

that grows atop Haleakalā on Maui may have first arrived in Hawai'i as the tiny seed of a simple daisy.

The end result of evolution by natural selection is speciation, new species. If a single species gives rise to many new species, scientists say that the ancestral species has "radiated." If each species in the radiation has a different habit, the complex of species is called an "adaptive radiation."

One of Hawaiʻi's most famous adaptive radiations is that of the honeycreepers, a family of birds unique to our islands. At least 20 species of honeycreepers, each distinguished by its method of feeding, are known. These are all the result of speciation events that can be traced back to a single ancestral species. That bird was probably an insect eater with a simple, straightforward beak. In time, bill shapes evolved as the birds foraged in a variety of habitats.

Birds feeding on hard seeds developed short, stout beaks for cracking and crushing. Nectar sippers evolved with long, thin bills for probing flowers. The bills of insect eaters are slightly curved and easily pick into bark crevices. Feather colors developed over time with similar specialization and variety. Remarkably, as species and habitat evolved together and influenced each other, certain flowers changed form, matching the shape of a bird's bill.

From the few colonizing seeds and spores that drifted here, nearly 1,000 species and subspecies of flowering plants have evolved, as have 4,000 insect species from 250 immigrant insect species; more than 1,000 land shells from perhaps 25 colonizing species; and 80 bird species from 15 or so ancestral species.

Hawaiʻi evolved as a relatively gentle place where snails, insects and birds dominated the fauna. No large predators reached these shores. Only two somewhat reclusive mammals, the bat and the seal, became established here. Chemical defenses in plants were reduced: the spicy scents of plants such as those in the mint family, of which there are about fifty native species, were lost altogether or were weakened over time.

Hawaiian trees have neither poisonous sap nor rough bark, both considered "defensive" mechanisms elsewhere. Deep, clinging root systems were replaced with spreading roots that utilize the thin layer of soil covering lava. Insects and birds evolved without wings and lived on the ground, perhaps because there were few or no ground predators. Human intrusion and the arrival of countless alien species now spell disaster for hundreds of vulnerable native species.

Just Wondering

The theory of adaptive radiation challenges scientists with fascinating questions about evolution: how do we explain, for example, the changes in genes of colonizing populations of species over time as plants and animals encounter new environments? How do we account for species like the honeycreepers and the tree snails that have evolved remarkable variety and specialization while other species, such as the kōlea, *and the* honu, *seem to remain "locked in" as a single species?*

Views

"The increasing inroads of man into the Hawaiian forests will, of course, take their toll in extinction of the Hawaiian [endemic species] . . . , but the main reason for their disappearance will be that they are delicate products of evolutionary campaigns won without opposition. Plants and animals from the continents are forged in the furnaces of stiff competition, and thus lantana and guava, mynah birds and sparrows, can outperform and displace the fragile inventions of adaptive radiation on islands."

(S. Carlquist, 1980)

Our Precious Natural Heritage

As a result of speciation, most of Hawai'i's native plant and animal species are unlike those found elsewhere in the world: they are unique to this land. Such plants and animals are called "endemic." What is singular about Hawai'i is that most—perhaps as many as 98 percent—of its prehuman plant and animal species are endemic, occurring nowhere else. Scientists believe that this percentage is higher than in any other place in the world. It is these endemic plants and animals that are the precious treasures of our Hawaiian natural heritage. Found nowhere else, they deserve our special awareness; imperiled as they are, they demand our care and our concern.

There are also plants and animals native to Hawai'i that occur naturally in other places as well. A visitor from Hawai'i feels quite at home on the tropical islands of the South Pacific, where many plants are familiar. A plant or animal that is native to a specific area but is also found elsewhere is called "indigenous." The indigenous *'ōhi'a lehua*, which gives us one of our most treasured "Hawaiian" flowers, and which is among the quickest to appear on bare lava flows following an eruption, is found on many other islands throughout the South Pacific. Added now to these endemic and indigenous species are the multitudes of exotic plants and animals introduced by people: they have altered much of the original Hawaiian landscape beyond recognition, and their long-term effects on the land are generally unknown.

This book is mainly about animals. The story of plants' arrival in Hawai'i awaits a book of its own. The animals discussed in the following chapters are examples of endemic, indigenous and exotic species in Hawai'i. Their stories illustrate how different animals have found their way to these islands and how they have fared under the conditions they have faced.

Tears of Salt

The Green Turtle

Hawaiian Name: *Honu*
Scientific Name: *Chelonia mydas*
Range: Native to Hawai'i

Lore and Legend

Honu are this land's ancient, gentle ones. At a time when only gods and winds moved on the land, *honu* hovered among the islands and slid onto empty beaches.

Legend tells us that when the fishing god Kū'ulakai lay dying he called his son 'Ai'ai to his mat and gave him four magical objects that would hold care over all fish: a cowry shell, a hook, a stick, a stone.

Kū'ulakai directed 'Ai'ai to visit each island and mark sites near the sea where fish would be plentiful. Then, with death so near, there was little speaking left. Kū'ulakai pressed his face against his son's and breathed life's final breath into the boy's nostrils. The *mana* (spiritual power) of father passed to chosen son, and *lehua* blossoms scattered in the dark clouds of Kāne.

And so the son began his travels, starting where the morning light first touches these islands at Kumukahi at the easternmost tip of the Big Island and on to where the final light of evening flickers off cliffs at Lehua Island in the far northwest.

When on Lāna'i, at Ka'ena, he marked a rock, and the rock stirred and turned into a turtle. Thus, says the legend, the *honu* first came to these islands. To this day, the power of the land draws them to lay their eggs on these soft beaches.

Much later, when humans arrived and men fished Island waters, they built altars to give prayers of thanks at the sites 'Ai'ai had marked as sacred and generous places. *Honu* were often the *'aumākua* (guardian spirits) of these areas and of the families that lived there. One such *'aumakua*, who was known by the name Kauila, made her home at Punalu'u Bay on the island of Hawai'i and was beloved by the people of this area. Kauila could change to human form and care for children playing along the shoreline.

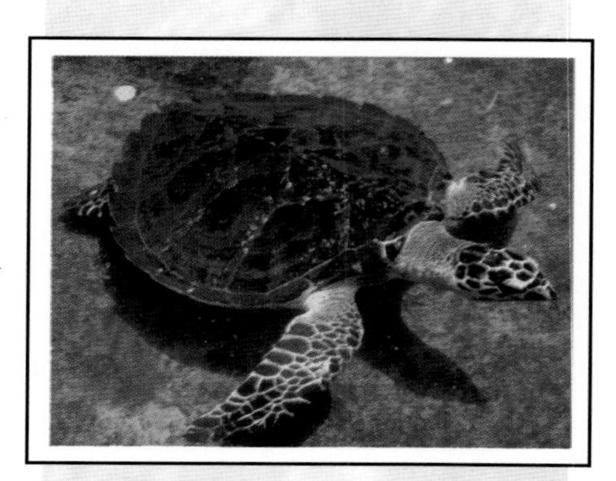

Honu 'ea *(hawksbill turtle)*

The gleaming shell of the *honu* was reserved for *ali'i*. Bracelets and fishhooks were fashioned from shell, as were special ceremonial objects such as the ringed decorations stacked on the staff of a *kāhili* (royal standard) that marked the presence of a chief. Kamehameha the Great drank his medicine from a beautiful turtleshell cup.

The shell of the turtle is richer in color than that of the tortoise and has been much valued by all peoples. When books were first printed in Hawai'i in the 1820s, the *ali'i* preferred *honu* shell bookcovers to plain paper or *kapa* (tapa) cloth editions. The

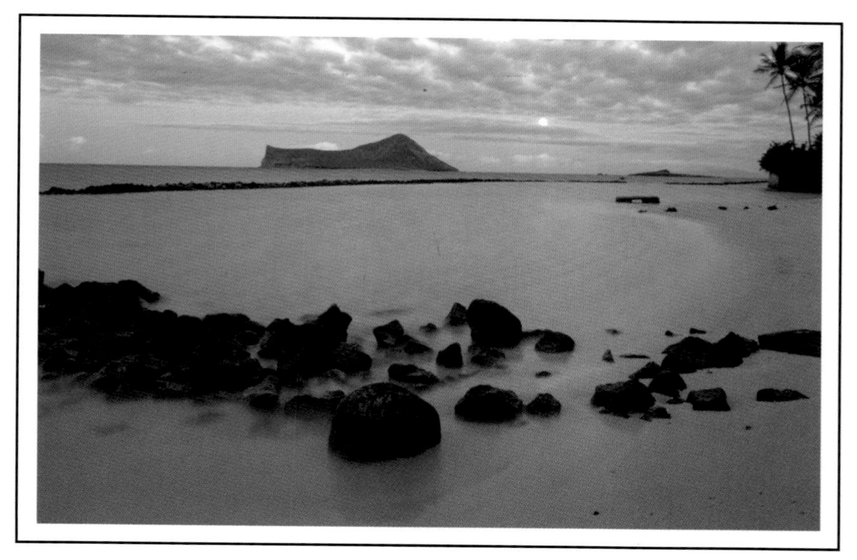

Turtle enclosure at Waimānalo Beach (Mānana [Rabbit] Island in background), where captured turtles were kept for chiefs

shells used were those of the *honu ʻea* (hawksbill turtle), now a rarity in Hawaiian waters and almost driven to extinction worldwide.

Hawaiians carefully regulated *honu* fishing through a strict set of *kapu* (prohibitions) that determined when turtles were taken, who could eat them and how their shells were used.

Food

Very young turtles live away from land at the ocean surface and feed on small jellyfish, Portuguese man-of-wars, and *limu* (seaweed). Mature turtles are vegetarians and spend hours each day grazing the underwater meadows of *limu* on coral reef and rocky shoreline. An adult turtle can stay submerged, resting or sleeping, for up to five hours, but usually surfaces more frequently to breathe.

Habitat

Though ponderous on land, weighing as much as four hundred bulky pounds, green turtles are swift and graceful in the sea, their primary habitat, and are able to swim faster than a child can run. *Honu* evolved over time in a land long safe from large predators, including humans. For many millions of years, turtles were the only reptiles to touch these islands. They came ashore undisturbed, for no dogs, rats, mongooses or people had yet arrived to threaten them.

Today the ancient prayers are hidden in the old language of the land, and the *honu* shy away from beaches that no longer are theirs. Instead, they migrate up the Hawaiian chain some eight hundred miles to the old, remote northwestern islands, where they bury their eggs. Unlike green turtles in other parts of the

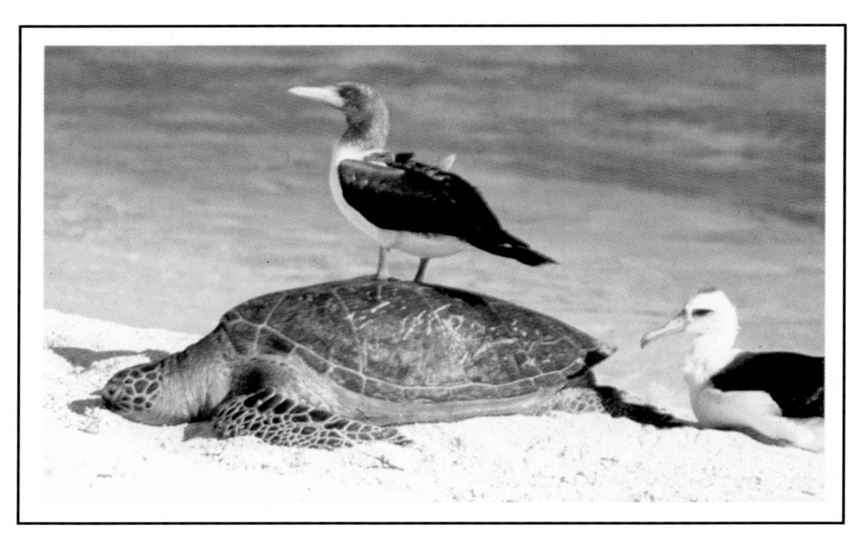

Green turtle basks with birds on Laysan Island.

world, however, Hawaiian *honu* still leave the sea during the day, pushing themselves up sheltered island beaches to doze and bask in the sun for hours before returning to the water.

Reproduction

Egg-laying, however, takes place in the dark. Each time a *honu* leaves the night sea and heaves up to hollow out her nest in the warm Hawaiian sand, she reenacts the ancient shift of a species from water to land, made possible by the egg. It was the evolution of the egg, that little movable pond contained in a protective shell, that allowed reptiles to reproduce away from water. Without the egg, the land would have remained empty of larger life forms—covered with plants, crawling with insects, but without reptiles, birds and mammals.

Just Wondering

Turtles and crocodiles return to land to lay their eggs. Frogs and toads return to water to lay their eggs. Why?

Green turtles in Hawai'i mate every two or three years. The breeding season runs from May through August, with the female setting several nests during the period. A male and female mate in the clear sea beneath the clearer sky and then separate, with the male continuing his ways of wandering and feeding that remain only partly understood by scientists.

The egg-bearing female returns to the beach of her own birth to lay her leathery eggs. She slides ashore at night, her eyes squinted shut, and trudges up the slanting sand to well above the high-tide line. Her cumbersome body, thick beneath its heart-shaped shell, shoves slowly up the shore; she frequently stops, wheezing and gasping in the spongy sand.

Turtle nesting sites are called rookeries. The nest must be out of reach of salt water that would kill the eggs. Shore grass and a certain amount of dampness in the sand prevent cave-ins as the female digs the pit that is to contain up to one hundred gray-white eggs. Often, the site of her nest slopes downward toward the water; this downward slant seems to help the hatchlings scamper to the relative safety of the ocean.

Female turtles dig down past the dry top layer of sand into the moisture below. The dampness of the deeper sand makes digging easier and also seems to contribute to regulating the temperature of the eggs. It is a slow, rhythmic, laborious digging: first her front flippers then her hind flippers stroke back the sand and shove it farther behind her. The completed hollow is wide and deep, some four feet across and two feet into the sand bank. By the time she has completed her nesting chamber, the female sea turtle will have moved well over a ton of sand.

Now, to form her nesting chamber in the firm sand, she turns and backs her way into the pit. Curving the ends of her hind flippers, she cuts away the sand, a cupful at a time, until she has formed a jar-shaped hole to hold the eggs. Then she begins to lay, one or two at a time, dropping as many as one hundred round, leathery eggs into the nesting hole.

Female turtle sweeps clean her next site.

The turtle has been working for hours in the starry darkness, but her task is not done. She must cover the nest site and erase traces of it. Using the wide, powerful swimming strokes of her front flippers, she sweeps the area smooth, hiding signs of her hidden offspring. She may move off and disturb the sand farther along the slope, creating the false impression of another nesting site.

This is her final protective task. From this point the offspring are on their own. The female will soon return to fill new nests

nearby, as many as five or six times in her laying season, but she will not care for the hatchlings.

She tractors her way back to the incoming waves, plowing a wide rut in the dark sand as she heads to the glimmering sea.

Just Wondering

Of all living reptiles, turtles are the most ancient. Can we look at a Hawaiian turtle without feeling awe and wonder as we sense a gigantic stretch of time in its bulky, prehistoric shape and birdlike features? in the four-billion-year-old water it inhabits? in the starlight that has taken millions, perhaps billions of years to travel through space to reach this beach and make the turtle's night shell gleam?

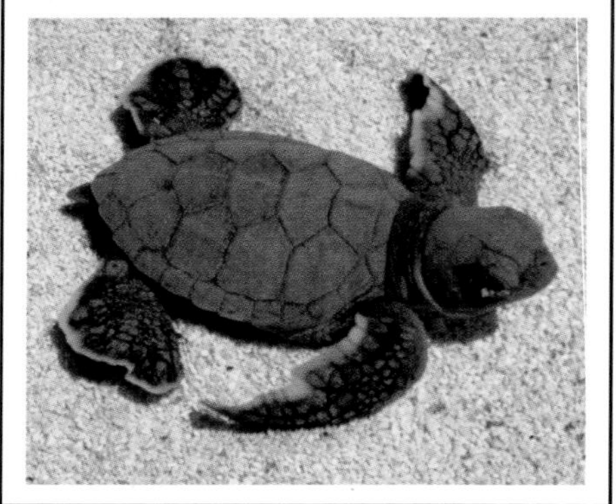

Hustling hatchling

Sand temperature overrides genetics in determining the sex of embryonic turtles. Scientists have found that low nest temperatures (below twenty-eight degrees centigrade) produce all male hatchlings. High temperatures (30 to 32 degrees centigrade) produce all females. A moderate temperature level of 28 to 29 degrees produces a 50/50 sex ratio. On beaches where nests are placed among protective shrubs or trees, temperatures tend to be low. In Hawai'i, the shores of the northwestern islands, where most turtles nest, are quite empty of vegetation, which results in an equal sex ratio in Hawaiian green turtles.

The egg white of the turtle contains 16 percent less water than that of a chicken. Additional moisture is absorbed from the sand, ensuring the well-being of the young turtle. The yolk, however, is considerably larger than that of the hen. This rich food nourishes the developing turtle during the long incubation period.

After about two months of incubation, the little turtles wriggle up through the sand in a flurry of scampering into the early morning dim. In Hawai'i, predators do not pose a great threat to the skittering hatchlings, but elsewhere in the world, the tiny turtles must scurry madly to the sea to avoid being snatched up by the sharp beaks of swooping seabirds blurring above, clawed tight and dragged down dark burrows by quick crabs, or slurped up by prowling iguanas. Once the turtles reach the water safely, large fish and sharks threaten them continually as they spend their first four years drifting the high sea far from land. Scientists estimate that only one turtle of a thousand newborn will survive to adulthood.

We don't really know how many years it takes for a hatchling to reach maturity. Green turtles are vegetarians most of their lives and grow slowly. Experts believe that turtles wander widely for several years, living away from land at sea. As they grow older, they take up residency along a particular coastline and may live there for many years. The connection of an individual *honu* to a certain area is strong and long-lasting. It may live there twenty-five to thirty years before returning to its shores of birth

Pushing forth to high seas, high dangers

to begin its own cycle of reproduction. There is much that remains a mystery about this land's ancient, gentle ones:

Just Wondering

"But where do they spend those first years at sea? This is one of the great remaining mysteries in marine natural history. The mystery is common to all sea turtles in all oceans they inhabit. Solving it may prove more difficult than locating the haunts of the chambered nautilus or the midocean breeding grounds of freshwater eels, both of which are becoming fairly well known."

(J. Culliney, 1988)

It is estimated that fewer than two hundred thousand mature female green turtles remain, roaming the world's seas where previously there were millions. Turtles face constant dangers: speedboat propellers hack into them; birthday party balloons and plastic bags, mistaken for jellyfish, clog their intestines; inappropriate coastal developments take away their nesting sites; scraps of fishing line and netting entangle, strangle and drown them; ugly, deadly tumors bulge up on their bodies; and humans still kill them for their meat and shells. But thanks to federal and state protections, the *honu* are making a strong comeback in Hawaiian waters, and their survival as a species seems secure.

As we sit on our surfboards awaiting a wave, or skim over the evening sea, practicing for next Sunday's canoe race, we often are thrilled to get a glimpse of a turtle bobbing up for breath nearby. It wheezes softly, gazes in silence, then disappears. Only a few years ago we saw none: we have sensed the emptiness of extinction! But the *honu* are back, and we must commit ourselves to safeguarding them forever.

Views

"I've seen a species I know and love grow in numbers and become more accepting of people. The increasing numbers of nesting turtles are an example of what can happen when the state, federal government and community work together to protect a species."

(George Balazs, Sea Turtle Researcher, National Marine Fisheries Service, National Wildlife, *June/July, 1999)*

More Turtle Facts

Turtle meat is much appreciated by a variety of predators, including humans. The flesh of the hawksbill turtle, however, can be very toxic at times and risky to eat. Green turtles, named after their greenish brown fat, which is used to make a much-esteemed soup, were commonly caught at sea and kept in the holds of sailing ships as a convenient, nonperishable meat supply. Tipped onto their backs, the turtles stayed alive for a long time, flippers waving slowly like wings flying nowhere, until they were slaughtered for a shipboard meal.

Just Wondering

Why is turtle fat green?

Research suggests that turtle nesting may help to maintain the health of beaches and dunes. Organic nutrients left by unhatched turtle eggs make sand and soil more fertile, promoting the growth of beach plants, which in turn protect sandy shores from erosion.

Honu now shun remote beaches on the island of Lānaʻi that once provided nesting grounds. The area known as Polihua was formerly a prime turtle nesting site. One story includes a description of turtles there as being so big that three people could easily ride on their backs. Today, Polihua Beach is rarely visited by turtles. As access to the beach became easier and the protective *kapu* of the past were discarded, it is likely many more *honu* were eaten than ever before. Another key factor in *honu* decline at Polihua seems to be the gnarly *kiawe* (mesquite) trees that grow down to the water's edge, pushing dense webs of tough roots into the nesting sites:

Views

"You dig through the surface and you find this mat of kiawe roots. If a turtle were trying to dig a nesting hole with its flippers, it couldn't get through."

(George Balazs, Sea Turtle Researcher, National Marine Fisheries Service, Honolulu Advertiser, *November 23, 1998)*

Often, when pulled from the water, green turtles seem to weep. The tears are produced by special glands and contain high levels of salt. The shedding of these tears lowers the salt level in their bodies.

Just Wondering

The human body is also a reservoir, with salt water making up some 60 to 70 percent of our weight. When we taste our tears, blood from a cut, sweat from our play, the fluids are salty. Are our salty body waters a physical memory of life's distant beginnings in the sea?

In some areas, turtles are afflicted by a disease called fibropapilloma, which produces fleshy tumors that frequently lead to death. The cause of this disease is not clearly understood. The epidemic spread of the disease is of particular concern in certain waters of Hawaiʻi and Florida. Research is under way to find ways to prevent or control this disease, possibly through the development of vaccines.

Just Wondering

Researchers are struggling to determine why this disease affects certain turtles and not others. Could humans indirectly be the cause? By allowing all matter of waste into the sea are people creating this problem?

In 1973, the Endangered Species Act made the *honu* and several other species of sea turtle *kapu* (protected). It is a crime to catch, kill, or keep a sea turtle. With government permission, researchers have attached satellite transmitters to critically endangered hawksbill turtles to track their migration patterns. These transmitters are expensive—about $3500 each, not including the cost of satellite tracking time. Anyone seeing a tagged turtle or one with a transmitter fastened to its shell should call George Balazs of the National Marine Fisheries Service in Honolulu at 808-983-5733. One of the few remaining nesting sites in Hawai'i for these rare turtles lies a stone's throw from the Azeka Place Shopping Center in Kīhei, Maui. Other Hawaiian species protected by the Endangered Species Act include—as of 1999—40 animals and 292 plants that are listed as endangered. Another 14 species are listed as threatened.

The ancient, worn down islands strung toward the northwest from Ni'ihau to Kure Atoll are specially protected areas, and it is to these islands that *honu* now migrate to mate and bury their eggs. These 132 islets, atolls, reefs and rocks extend 1,523 miles to the northwest of Ni'ihau

Laysan Island, flattened by erosion

Laysan Island monk seal, snoozing

and vary in size from a few acres to two square miles. In 1909, the Northwestern Hawaiian Islands National Wildlife Refuge was established to provide a permanently safe environment for turtles, the Hawaiian monk seal and many species of birds. The monk seal was nearly exterminated in the 1800s by hunters; today, monk seals are estimated to have increased in number to over two thousand. Many rare birds, including the Laysan finch, the Laysan duck and the millerbirds and finches of Nihoa are sheltered by the refuge. In the past twenty-five years the number of nesting female turtles on a small group of islands called the French Frigate Shoals, located nearly 500 miles northwest of Honolulu, has grown from fifty to five hundred. Great news!

Views

"Over the past five years, I've seen turtles everywhere around O'ahu. It's time to take a look for establishing a protocol for bringing turtles back into our culture. I can remember my uncles catching turtles and my aunties preparing them. But that has been lost over several generations.

There are generations who have lost the knowledge of how to catch, clean and prepare turtles. And I resent the singular 'warm and fuzzy' representation of turtles being made in some educational efforts. Our children are being brainwashed. Turtle primarily was a respected and required part of our menu."

(William Aila, Native Hawaiian fisherman, Honolulu Advertiser, *June 7, 1998)*

"Regarding the June 7 article on the push to legalize hunting of green turtles, a threatened species. The 'Hawaiian culture' argument is almost ludicrous. Just because it was popular in the past to kill the turtles for their meat and body parts does not mean it is OK today. Cultures evolve; methods of gathering food change. Like it or not, in today's Hawai'i, there is no need to kill turtles to feed oneself or one's family.

Some Pacific cultures used to practice cannibalism. Should we now legalize murder so that these cultures can return to cannibalism?"

(Clay W. Valverde, Letter to the Editor, Honolulu Advertiser, *June 11, 1998)*

Wave-like "ripples" trace the sandy "wake" of a female turtle, returning to sea from a night visit on shore.

A Treeful of Rainbows

The O'ahu Tree Snail

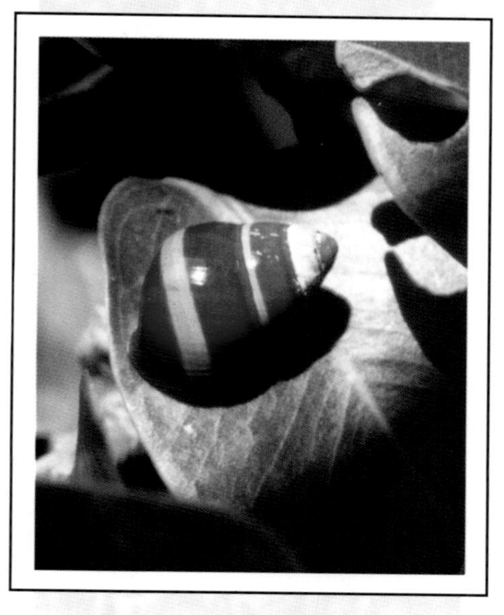

Hawaiian Name: *Pūpū, pūpū kani oe, kāhuli*
Scientific Name: Family Achatinellidae
Range: Endemic to O'ahu

Arrival in Hawai'i

Unlike the green turtle, which wanders far, sometimes thousands of miles from the sands of its birth, the little endemic tree snail tends to stay put. Some spend their entire lives in a single tree.

Many endemic Hawaiian tree snails trace their more distant origins to other islands in the South Pacific but have lived and evolved in Hawai'i for untold thousands of years. In addition to *Achatinella*, Hawai'i has some eight hundred other species of land snails found nowhere else on Earth.

How such a slow creeper could first make its way to Hawai'i, tiny specks of islands hidden in the middle of the world's greatest ocean, delights the imagination.

Migratory birds like the *kōlea* and any number of ducks and geese began to spend a good part of the year on this then-nameless land and on other Pacific islands, returning to their home continents to breed. The first small snails may have hitched a ride attached to just such birds. In historic times, snails have occasionally been found stuck to the feathers of arriving birds or pasted in dry mud to a waterfowl's webbed foot. The slime of the snail seals the animal in its protective shell and glues the shell to the bird.

While the tree snail may not wander far compared with the green turtle, its evolutionary journey has been amazingly long. The turtle has probably changed very little in the millions of years it has slid through our island waters. In contrast, tree snails have evolved individual species of great variety and specialization.

Habitat

Just as the Hawaiians later gave individual names to each of the winds that visited a single valley, depending on its origin and direction, the rain or mist it frequently carried, its strength or the scents it brought, so too did the tree snails carefully mark themselves over time as a unique and precious detail of a specific landscape and location. Countless varieties of these graceful snails evolved in the Hawaiian Islands. In each valley, on each ridge and sometimes even on a single small stand of trees, unique varieties evolved, different in color and pattern from all others.

The valley of Nu'uanu, for example, which runs up toward the *pali* (cliff) behind Honolulu, was once home to at least twenty-five varieties of snails, each a distinctly different shape, color and

Pelekunu Valley, Moloka'i

pattern depending on where in the valley its ancestors had evolved. Hawaiians of old believed that the forest sang with the songs of these many tree snails. There are beautiful stories and chants in Hawaiian about the throbbing call of the colored snails.

Just Wondering

Malacologists—scientists who specialize in the study of snails—question these stories. They point out that snails are not physically equipped to sing and that many of the forest songs are now known to come from the nearly two hundred native species of crickets. But the belief persists, particularly among Hawaiians who are very keen observers of detail in nature. Perhaps it's worth a second look?

Tree snails were once plentiful from the high uplands *ma uka* (inland) down through the lowland valleys and dry woodlands to the nearby sea. Many species are now extinct. Fire-clearing of land for agricultural use by early Hawaiians is thought to have caused significant habitat destruction and a decline in the number of lowland snails. The introduction of the rat and pig also affected their numbers. Later, *haole* (foreign) visitors and settlers brought cattle, goats, horses and many other animals to the islands. Trampling and overgrazing of undergrowth in native habitats accounted for much of the loss of snails. With the arrival of alien plants, predators and human collectors, the snails easily fell prey.

Snail shells vary in color and pattern.

Views

"[T]he numerous herds of cattle rushing with their extended horns through the forests in all directions have, under our observations, nearly extinguished many fine species [of tree snails] that we had formerly found in abundance in the same localities."

(D. Frick, 1856)

The scientific name *Achatinella* means "little agate" and nicely describes the smooth, clearly colored shell of these forest gems. Early travelers to the islands commented on the beautiful decorative effects of many colored snails dotting the leaves and limbs of native trees. One observer described them as a treeful of tiny rainbows.

Food

Tree snails become active at night or during periods of heavy rain. They are grazers, curving slowly up the undersides of leaves, feeding earnestly on microscopic fungi that grow especially on certain native trees. Tiny rasping teeth scrape leaf surfaces without causing damage. During dry days, when sunshine hardens their food, snails seal themselves against a limb or leaf, their delicately patterned shells hung in motionless decoration.

Reproduction

Each snail is hermaphroditic, meaning both male and female, but usually two snails must meet and mate before an offspring results. Snails breed throughout the year, sometimes producing as many as six or seven offspring during that period. As a rule, only a single young is born at a time. Many tree snails produce as few as four offspring every year.

While most mollusks produce eggs, this tiny snail is born alive, housed in its own shell, which, in delicate, shiny patterning, is a miniature replica of its parent's shell. The young snail and parent are sometimes found on the same leaf, sliding along slowly side by side. Top speed for a Hawaiian tree snail is about three inches a minute.

Tree snails evolved over millions of years in a delicately balanced world with few natural enemies. In such a sheltered habitat there was no need to hurry—to escape a predator or produce large numbers of offspring.

Today there are very few tree snails left. Hiking the high hills, you'll be very lucky to spot one. In 1981, the *Achatinella* snails of O'ahu were listed among the twelve most critically endangered species in the world. Of the forty-one recognized species of endemic tree snails on the island of O'ahu, seventeen are presumed extinct and the remaining twenty-four are listed as endangered.

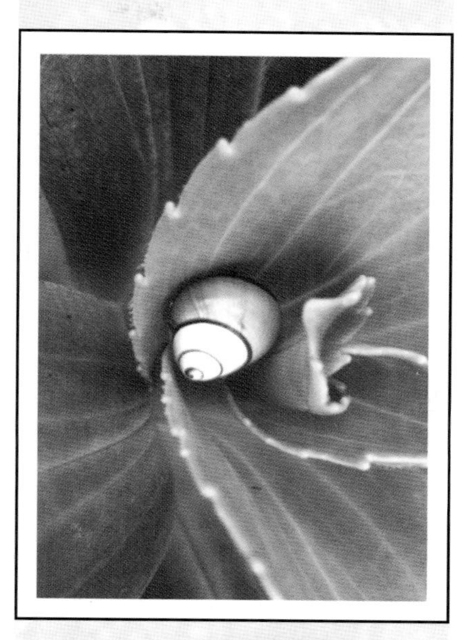

All species of endemic tree snails on O'ahu are either endangered or presumed extinct.

The tiny tree snail: born alive one at a time

Just Wondering

Did the forest songs disappear with the extinctions of these little creatures?

More Tree Snail Facts

Lei made of the "little agates" decorating native necks, ankles and wrists caught the eye of a British captain, George Dixon, who visited Oʻahu in 1786. He traded a single nail for a single *lei.* When he returned to Europe, the enterprising captain took the *lei* apart and sold each shell for $40—an extraordinary amount of money in those days—to eager purchasers.

Rats have been a terrible, silent enemy of many endemic species in Hawaiʻi. The stowaway Polynesian rat, slipping off early voyaging canoes and into fragile tree snail habitats, caused great destruction:

Views

"During the wet season nothing in the plains is safe from rats. . . . During the last months of the wet season in Welehu, Makaliʻi, and Kaelo [March–June], the rat makes its nest in the potato hills and returns to the mountains in the month of Kaulua [June–July] as it begins to grow warm. By the month of Nana [July–August] a large number of rats have returned to the mountain, and by the month of Welo [August–September]there are no rats left in the plain."

(K. Kepelino, 1932)

Piles of rat-crushed shells

In the 1870s, a second species, the introduced tree-climbing black rat, became widespread on Oʻahu. Pale piles of crushed shells lay beneath bushes that had previously been home to many snails. Rodents soon began to pose a direct threat to people: rat infestations on all islands became severe, and bubonic plague, spread by fleas that had bitten into infected rats, caused its first human deaths in the Hāmākua area of the Big Island as early as 1883. Numerous

The 1900 Chinatown fire (top) and aftermath (bottom)

fatalities were reported in Honolulu in December 1899 and January 1900. In the third week of the new century, a fire, lit to rid the disease from the Chinatown district of Honolulu, burst out of control and burned thirty-four square acres of central Honolulu to a smolder. Nearly five thousand

Broken rainbows: a boxful, a bucketful

homeless people camped on the grounds of Kawaiaha'o Church until they eventually were relocated. Black rats are now abundant on all eight main Hawaiian islands—from the seashore to the highest peaks of Mauna Loa and Mauna Kea.

»»»»»»»»»»»»»»»

Overcollecting by humans is considered a primary factor leading to the disappearance of the Hawaiian tree snail. While early Hawaiian *lei*-making using the snails probably had little impact on their numbers, later collectors became greedy. Between 1850 and 1900, a period of "land shell fever," a favorite pastime of students at O'ahu College (later known as Punahou School) was to head to the hills on shell-collecting outings. Bucketfuls of jeweled snails were brought back and vast collections assembled. Some private collections included up to one hundred thousand specimens.

Views

"The rarest days of all were those we spent hunting for tree snails. . . . I still feel the exhilaration of those excursions, the zest of coming upon a hidden surprise of nature, some fine specimen of those beautiful shells, each ridge, each valley revealing its peculiar variety . . . ."

(Oliver Emerson, Punahou School graduate; quoted in Kay, 1972)

"[D]uring a recent visit to the locality, during a few minutes I collected several hundred specimens, picking them from trees and low bushes as rapidly as one would gather huckleberries from a prolific field."

(D. Baldwin, Punahou School graduate, in Hawaiian Annual, *1887)*

Another arrival to Hawai'i began its destructive feasting on endemic snails more recently. In 1955, a carnivorous mollusk, known as the cannibal snail or by its

Euglandia rosea, *or cannibal snail*

Cannibal snail attacks tree snail: fear not, the tree snail was saved.

scientific name, *Euglandina rosea*, was brought to Hawai'i from Florida to control the huge African snail, a World War II arrival that had become a serious garden pest. The cannibal snail soon moved to the cooler uplands and developed a taste for the little *Achatinella*. The results have been disastrous. Many scientists had opposed the introduction of the cannibal snail. Sadly, scant fieldwork took place before the snails were introduced to see what the effects might be.

▸▸▸▸▸▸▸▸▸▸▸▸▸▸▸▸

The cannibal snail is one of several predators introduced to help eliminate the African snail, one of the world's largest land snails, with a shell length measuring up to six inches and an appetite to match its size. Originally from East Africa, where they are commonly eaten by humans, they were spread throughout the Pacific for use as food on islands occupied by the Japanese during World War II. These snails arrived in Hawai'i through the mail from Japan in 1938. Known then as "Japanese snails," they were raised as a delicacy for local restaurants. They quickly became a common garden nuisance, however, reproducing at a phenomenal rate. It has been calculated that one snail can theoretically produce 11 million offspring in five years. In mid-1938, the *Honolulu Star-Bulletin* ran this front-page headline: "War is Declared on Giant Snails—100 Men Will Start Work to Eradicate Pests in Pauoa Valley and on Maui." The African snail remains both a problem in our gardens today and a serious carrier of diseases, some of which endanger humans. Over the years, several species of beetles, including—unsuccessfully—the Japanese firefly, have been introduced to control this snail.

African snail

Another nasty snail pest that arrived in Hawai'i as recently as 1989 is the apple snail, native to South America. This mollusk feeds aggressively on taro and is a

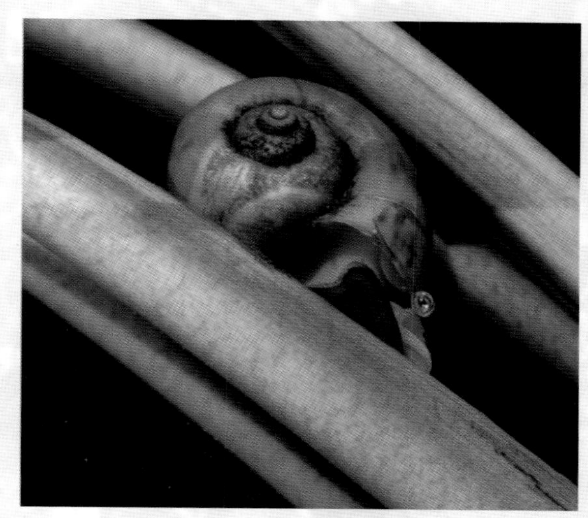

Apple snail

threat to any plant growing in or near water. The apple snail is a pest to farmers wherever taro is grown in Hawai'i. In late December, 1995, the shocking report came that someone had dumped bucketfuls of apple snails along several of Kaua'i's pristine streams. Many volunteers helped to collect and kill the pests.

Today, the Bishop Museum in Honolulu, noted for its vast collections, has only a very few land snail *lei* from Hawai'i. One is a beautiful brownish white *lei* made from Kaua'i snails that lived on the ground, rather than in trees. All species of these land snails are probably now extinct.

▸▸▸▸▸▸▸▸▸▸▸▸▸▸▸▸

High above Mākua Valley in O'ahu's Wai'anae Mountains, the State Department of Land and Natural Resources is staging what may be a last stand for one species of *Achatinella*. Sheets of corrugated aluminum enclose two 40- by 100-foot compounds, providing a safe if tiny haven of native plants for about fifty tree snails, hardly enough for a treeful of rainbows. Defense systems include exterior trays of rat poison, a salt trough, and electric shock lines to stop cannibal snails from getting into the exclosure. Too little, too late? These efforts come after decades of U.S.

Curved and colored like a wilting fern, this snail is easy to overlook.

Army abuse of Mākua as a training site for live-fire military operations. Year after year, wildfires caused by artillery bombings have scorched *Achatinella* habitats, causing incalculable damage to snail populations and the native plants they depend on. A University of Hawaiʻi professor expressed some doubt as to the outcome of the preservation efforts:

Views

"It has taken more than 15 years of lawsuits and bad publicity to curtail the Army's 65-year history of bombing and burning in Mākua Valley. I'm heartened by their recent emphasis on environmental monitoring and protection in Hawaiʻi; they have hired an excellent crew to do it. The state's efforts to protect the tree snails above Mākua Valley are an exciting experiment, and we can only hope that it isn't too late."

(Michael G. Hadfield, Professor of Zoology and Director Kewalo Marine Laboratory, personal communication to author)

Mākua Valley, Oʻahu, shows fire damage after Army training. Fires caused by people do vast damage to habitats each year in Hawaiʻi. Alien plants adapted to wildfires spring back and soon dominate a landscape. Unlike some continental ecosystems, Hawaiian forests and scrublands do not need fire to germinate seeds and renew.

Precious snails up in smoke: Mākua Valley on fire

Once a Wondrous Ruckus

The Hawaiian Crow

Hawaiian Name: *'Alalā*
Scientific Name:
Corvus hawaiiensis
Area of Origin:
Endemic to the Island of Hawai'i

Arrival in Hawai'i

Perhaps the rage of a prehistoric storm flung a flock of crows toward these remote islands. By remarkable chance, two or three of the heavy, brownish black birds survived the thrashing winds and pounding rains, were thrown to the ground, and lived to breed and nest and establish a colony of their kind.

Lore and Legend

Most birds, including the *'alalā*, were eaten in old Hawai'i. Exceptions were said to be the meat-feeding hawks and owls, whose flesh was deemed bad-tasting. *'Alalā*, and many other birds, were snared or caught with poles, the ends of which were smeared with the gummy sap of the breadfruit tree. When a bird perched on the stick, its feet stuck. Many birds were stoned or caught by net as flocks in flight. The little *koloa* (Hawaiian duck) was squeezed by its legs and yanked down by a diver who had approached underwater, breathing through a snorkel-like hollow reed.

Just Wondering

Why do birds have both dark and white meat?

Hawaiians used the crows' shiny black feathers for making *kāhili*, and for dressing idols. Some other ceremonial uses of the feathers have been recorded, but the colored feathers of the honey-creepers were generally preferred. Captain Cook noticed several *'alalā* during his stay at Kealakekua Bay and noted in his journal that "two of these birds [were] tame . . . which [Hawaiians] told me were Eatooas (spirits) and refused everything I offered for them, cautioned me, at the same time, not to hurt or offend them."

Habitat

Corvus hawaiiensis is found on the Big Island and is the only surviving species of Hawaiian crow. Recently, fossils were discovered of two other species of crows that once lived on Maui and O'ahu. Each had a body size and bill shape different from its relatives on the other islands.

The full range of the *'alalā* in ancient times is not known, but, like the tree snail, the crow is thought to have evolved very slowly,

interacting over time in a highly specialized and delicate relationship with a specific habitat. This area on the Big Island of Hawai'i encompasses a narrow band of dry woodlands and *'ōhi'a lehua* forests along the Ka'ū and Kona highlands of Mauna Loa, extending up the coast beyond Hualālai to Pu'uwa'awa'a.

The leeward slopes of this land lean seaward in rough, broken fields of scrubby lava cut by clumps of dry forest. From ancient times, ribboning *ma kai* (seaward) off the great volcanic flanks, fiery flows of lava burned paths down through the forests, opening spaces in the landscape like channels between forested islands. These open spaces, interspersed with protective stands of native trees, became the accustomed habitat for the *'alalā*.

Food

Such islands of greenery, called *kīpuka*, provided shelter for the *'alalā* as they fed on the fruits of endemic plants that colonized the lava. These fruits, and those of the forest *'ie'ie* plant, were their principal food, and it is thought that the *'alalā* evolved in this habitat as an important distributor of seeds and pollinator of the *'ie'ie*, whose pinkish red flowers and ripe fruit were available at different elevations over the course of the year.

The *kīpuka* also evolved as microlaboratories where the force of evolution expressed itself in stunning detail. The lava, after cutting off a portion of vegetation from a larger field or forest, acted as a barrier in much the same way as does a saltwater channel between islands. These microenvironments often reveal wonderful examples of evolution at work: a single tree has been known to house a unique species of Hawaiian tree snail, and a single lava tube a one-of-a-kind cricket species.

Here, in this very confined area of the Big Island, squawking, flocking crows were once common. Up to twenty inches in length, with an adult weight of a pound and a half, the crow is one of the few large endemic Hawaiian birds to have survived into modern times. In flight, its flapping wings can be noisy or silent as it sails from limb to limb.

Just Wondering

Evolution is a mind-boggling force of change in species. How did the sluggish, ponderous, cold-blooded reptile make its evolutionary way to the high-fever intensity and grace of a bird in flight?

The call of the *ʻalalā* is a raw caw repeated rapidly. A flock cawing in unison was said to cause a wonderful ruckus. One observer called it the noisiest bird in the lower Kona forests at daybreak. Another observer, however, referred to the crow caw as being "generally mellow and musical . . . as if it were produced from a pair of reed pipes."

Views

"Scientists have identified over 50 vocalizations for this bird. They've got a whoop, holler, pop, whistle—all kinds of stuff unlike any other bird probably anywhere in the world."

(Keith Unger, Manager McCandless Ranch, Kona, Hawaiʻi, personal communication to author)

And like crows everywhere, flocking *ʻalalā* are bright, brash, busy, bossy, boisterous, bullish birds whose near extinction creates a huge blank space in the landscape of its original habitat. As with the extinction of any species, the biological richness of the world is diminished by its disappearance—and therewith the experience of human beings who in gratitude and wonder share that world.

Reproduction

To nest, *ʻalalā* move *ma uka* into the higher, damper inland forests where *koa* trees once were common. Hawaiian crows show strong pairing instincts and are exceedingly territorial; pairs return year after year to the same site to raise a new clutch. Like Hawaiian tree snails, *ʻalalā* live long lives and breed slowly, their low reproduction rate well suited to a world before human intrusion.

Nests, built of rough sticks and lined with grass and moss, are mostly placed in the high branches of tall *ʻōhiʻa lehua* trees near taller *koa* trees that serve as lookout posts and roosting sites.

Unfortunately, we know very little in detail of the normal habits of the *ʻalalā* in a healthy, undisturbed environment. We know more about aspects of its decline as a species, as is often the case with endemic Hawaiian species whose natural environments have been so drastically altered.

One observer of a nesting pair in the late 1930s described a

A solitary crow (top) perches in a high branch of a lookout tree; pairs of crows (bottom) build a nest in the same area year after year.

Crows leave eggs uncovered only briefly.

'Alalā *fledglings*

clutch of four to five eggs. The eggs were a pale, greenish blue, splotched with brown and occasional black flecks. Adults shared in the task of incubating the eggs, and only briefly were the eggs left uncovered. The bird that was not incubating the eggs remained near the nest for minutes at a time, preening its feathers.

Just Wondering

Scientists don't really know much about the origin of feathers. Where did they come from? How do they work? Why do birds preen continually?

'Alalā fledglings leave the nest before they are strong fliers and spend time on the ground or climbing in the lower-level vegetation while still being fed by their parents. They depend on the understory to shelter them from their main predator, the *'io* (Hawaiian hawk), and only gradually do they make their way into open areas to graze the endemic fruits that make up a large share of their diet.

In the wild, *'alalā* fledglings spend up to a year with their parents and other members of the flock, probably imprinting the behaviors of feeding and defense that evolved over thousands of years in a specific Hawaiian habitat. Researchers don't know exactly what it is that young crows learn during this phase of flock socialization, but suspect that part of it might involve teamwork tactics that deal with an attacking Hawaiian hawk, their natural enemy. A hawk will swoop in on an unsuspecting solitary crow and kill it quickly. But two or more crows working together can usually take on and thwart an attacking hawk. There are reports of *'alalā* in their natural state ganging up on a hawk and chasing it away.

'Io *(Hawaiian hawk)*

More ʻAlalā Facts

From the arrival of the first Polynesians, it seems that almost without exception, every change caused by humans to the *ʻalalā* environment—and there have been countless changes—had a negative impact on this bird. The total effect of all these changes is the near extinction of the species. Polynesians burned off large portions of the original dry lowland forest that was home to the *ʻalalā*. The little dark stowaway rats that made their way to Hawaiʻi on Polynesian canoes probably preyed on *ʻalalā* nestlings and fledglings. Later, the harvesting of sandalwood, that fragrant wood sold by Hawaiian *aliʻi* to Western merchants bound for the Orient, further modified dry-forest ecology at low and middle elevations. But the endemic crow, though affected by such changes, probably held its own until the early twentieth century, as suggested by the following observation:

Views

"When we were in Kona in 1891 the ʻalalā was numerous. They went in flocks and were most inquisitive, following the intruder with loud cawing. The least imitation of their cry brought them close in. We saw an amusing instance of this. A tethered horse on the mountain of Hualālai, neighing for company, brought a whole flock down around it. This trait has no doubt been exploited to their undoing. In the early 1890s as Kona became more closely settled, the farmers, exasperated by the depredations of the crows in feed pens and poultry yards, made war on it, capitalizing on its well known traits of curiosity. By imitating its call, many birds would easily be brought to the gun. Years later when on the bird survey in 1937, I found a great change. The birds were greatly reduced in numbers. I saw no flocks, only a few scattered individuals. The birds refused to answer my call, perhaps having learned the danger of it."

(George C. Munro, Co-founder, Hawaiʻi Audubon Society, 1960)

Cattle convert forest to pasture; scattered, broken koa *branches are all that remain.*

According to Munro's observations, raucous flocks of crows, once annoyingly common in the Kona region, had been reduced to scattered individuals by 1937. The decline continued for years, but few busy humans noticed their dire plight. In 1976, a particularly unfortunate event took place when an important nesting area on Hualālai was bulldozed to open up ranch land for cattle. By 1980, no nests remained at this site. In 1978, the total number of surviving *'alalā* was seventy-five. Ten years later, just eleven crows remained in a single secluded area of the McCandless Ranch in South Kona. Today, that number has climbed to thirty-three—three *'alalā* in the wild and thirty in captive breeding programs.

Fire burns exotic grasses hot and fast.

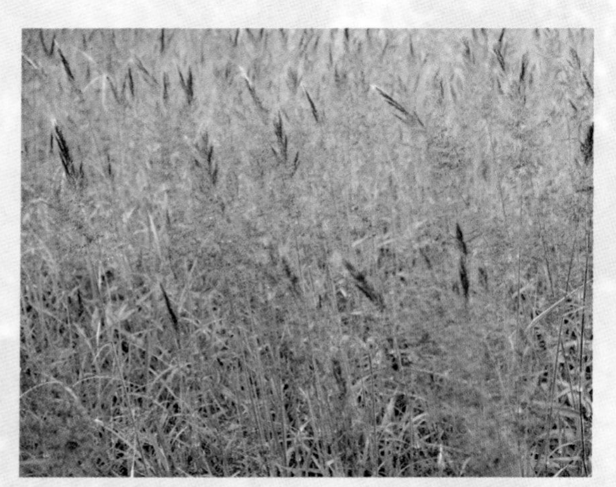

Red-top grass, introduced in 1895 from Cape of Good Hope

A major factor of *'alalā* decline is something as simple as grass. Unlike its North American cousins, which often are found in grassland areas, the Hawaiian crow evolved in a forested habitat, where both feeding and breeding took place. *'Alalā* swooped to adjoining lava fields, where native shrubs and bushes provided the fruits that made up much of their diet. Endemic types of grass filled these areas only sparsely. When ranchers later introduced exotic grasses to create pasture for cattle, a solid ground cover formed, blocking native plant seed germination. Native plants, lacking thorns or bad-tasting juices, were foraged out by grazing cattle, leaving the thin layer of soil beneath them exposed to the sun. The soil quickly dried out, causing further loss of habitat vegetation. Cattle sowed grass seeds with their droppings in open areas where native species had been disrupted. One common species of introduced grass, called fountain grass, wilts back annually, leaving withered tufts that easily burn, leading wildfires to surviving native plants. Several varieties of introduced grasses have a high resin content, which makes them blaze hot and fast. The small, fruit-bearing native shrubs, the primary food source for the *'alalā*, simply could not compete with the sturdy alien grasses.

Introduced animals have also changed the natural balance of plants and animals in the habitat the *'alalā* had come to rely on as a precise and fragile place, carefully built up over thousands of years by a distinct mix of species evolving together. Humans,

A single, silent injection (top) can bring death deep into native forests.

first Hawaiians and then Westerners, cleared the land for housesites, taro patches, farms, pastures and plantations, greatly reducing the forest acreage and biological diversity that supported the territorial crow. Like invading battalions, a succession of alien intruders followed: night-feeding, tree-climbing rats; herds of grazing cattle, goats and sheep; rooting, earth-churning pigs; bird-killing cats; day-feeding mongooses. And the most insidious of all, the frail, shrill mosquito, hatched from cattle water troughs and mud puddles gouged out by pigs. A mosquito's "bite" next to the eye of a native bird squirts in a deadly dose of avian malaria or bird pox, alien diseases against which Hawaiian species have no resistance.

Views

"The ʻōhiʻa lehua *gradually passes into the* koa *forest, if such it can still be called; for nowhere has the writer found such a pitiable sight as the* koa *forest presents in this district at about 3,000 feet up to 5,000 feet elevation. Here 90 per cent of these giant koa trees are dead; their huge limbs dangle in the air on pieces of fibrous strings of bark, ready to drop if stirred by the slightest breeze. The remaining 10 per cent of the trees are in a dying condition, and in a very few years the country will be entirely denuded. Huge masses of trunks and limbs are scattered over the ground, and it is really difficult to ride through this remnant of forest. . . . This condition is mainly due to the cattle, which have destroyed all the undershrubs and also injured the trees, which are then readily attacked by insects."*

(J.F. Rock, 1913)

Only thirty-three *ʻalalā* remain. Other bird species have dwindled this low, and lower, and been saved. There is hope, for example, in the story of the *nēnē*. In 1949, there were no more than thirty endemic *nēnē* geese left in the wild. Thanks to an international breeding program there are now an estimated eight hundred living free in the volcano area of the Big Island. For the *poʻouli*, a small member of the endemic Hawaiian honeycreeper family of birds living high in the forests above Hāna, Maui, the numbers are even more precarious. In the summer of 1998, only three could be found, two of which were caught and identified as female. Similarly, when the last remaining tree of the Molokaʻi cotton plant known as *kokoi* died, the only hope left for this beautiful red-flowered Hawaiian plant was a single branch earlier grafted onto another type of tree cotton. The tissue culture from this one branch may, with the help of modern scientific

Nēnē, *an example of the success of international breeding programs*

techniques, be used to propagate new plants, providing some hope for such critically endangered species.

Cloning is another tool that may be used to save endemic species. Cutting-edge technology at the University of Hawai'i startled the world in the summer of 1998 when lab researchers announced that they had successfully cloned fifty mice over three generations beginning with a "miracle" mouse named Cumulina. There is much hope that knowledge gained through such "local science" can extend benefits to our many endangered species.

Just Wondering

Has natural selection given way to human selection? Is evolution still functional? Are we about to enter an era in which humans can control their own nature as well as that of the biosphere as a whole? How far can humans go in fooling around with nature?

Views

"In the forest and bog country of Alaka'i on the island of Kaua'i there used to be a big population of a native bird called the 'ō'ō. They were described in 1891 as common, in 1903 as numerous, then by 1928 they were talked about as rare. By 1960 a survey could find only twelve of them, and by the 1980s they were down to two, and then to one—just like the Laysan teal, only this time the circumstance is truly terminally dire, because the one surviving Kaua'i 'ō'ō is a male, so that it is hard to envision a miracle of biological brinkmanship in the Alaka'i. Wildlife workers in the Alaka'i have spotted the last 'ō'ō in recent years, each time in much the same

place, one small black bird, singing and building a nest each year, making all the right moves of its species to attract a mate. But there seems to be no mate to attract, and there probably can never be. The ʻōʻō was photographed not long ago, in silhouette, alone. Its solitary song was tape-recorded from up close and played back in the forest the next day. The ʻōʻō, this lone black bird, flew to the source of the song and found nothing but a single, wingless black machine, singing."

(Gavan Daws, 1988)

Just Wondering

Extinction is a natural process that has occurred since the beginning of life on Earth. It is estimated that 99 percent of the plant and animal species that have ever lived are now extinct. The average life span of a species in the fossil record is about four million years. Many major groups of plants and animals that were once common became extinct and left no descendants. Are we overly concerned by the possible disappearance of species such as the honu, *the* ʻalalā *or the tiny tree snails? Tens of millions of dollars have been spent in our efforts to save the last crows, the last snails. Does it make sense?*

A lone silhouette: the last ʻōʻō?

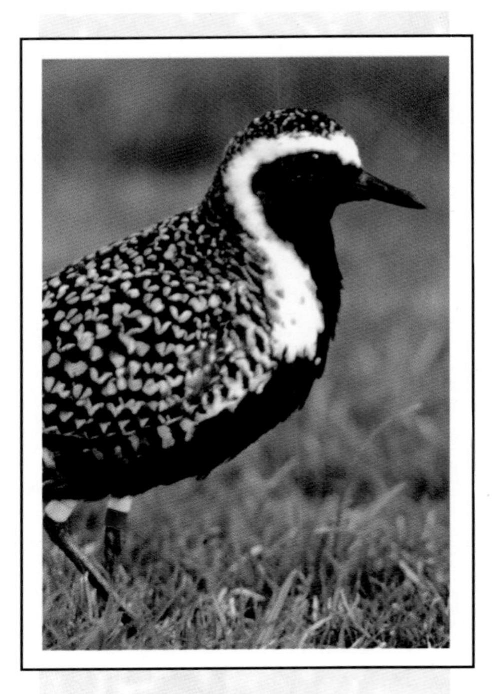

Hawaiian Name: *Kōlea*
Scientific Name: *Pluvialis fulva*
Range: Native to Hawai'i and other Pacific areas

MYSTERIOUS MIGRATIONS

The Pacific Golden Plover

ARRIVAL IN HAWAI'I

Unlike many animals, such as the tree snail and *'alalā*, that became established in Hawai'i long before the arrival of humans and that, over time, evolved specializations that now make them unique to this land, the *kōlea* may have changed very little in the thousands of years it has made its annual return to these and other Pacific islands. Like that of the green turtle, the *kōlea*'s ancient cycle of reproduction follows a yearly pattern of migration to and from Hawai'i. The *kōlea* leaves the Hawaiian Islands in late April to lay eggs in the tundra of the far north; rather than its ancient arrival here, it is the yearly departure of this bird from Hawai'i and its connection to another land that is noteworthy.

LORE AND LEGEND

Kōlea make their yearly migrations north from as far away as Australia and the central South Pacific. More than likely, the *kōlea* was one of the birds that helped guide Polynesian voyagers northward toward Hawai'i. Seeing the yearly return of this bird to its own islands, Polynesians must have been convinced there was land to the north. Departing *kōlea* may have helped lead them there.

For Hawaiians the *kōlea* was an *'aumakua.* In legend the *kōlea* served as messengers of the gods or, often working in pairs, as scouts for high chiefs carrying news from island to island.

The annual disappearance of the *kōlea* caused great wonder. Its egg, never having been seen, became symbolic of any question lacking an answer or problem without a solution. The English-language shrug-of-the-shoulders "Who knows?" has its Hawaiian-language equivalent in *'O ka hua o ke kōlea, aia i Kahiki*, "The egg of the *kōlea* is found somewhere far away."

The moist, oily meat of the *kōlea* was much appreciated in days past. Hawaiians were expert marksmen who could easily stone a *kōlea* from an impressive distance. *Kōlea* were also snared. An insect was hooked to a short, sharp stick attached to a long string, the end of which was tied to a *kōlea* stone that served as an anchor. When the *kōlea* swallowed the insect, the string jerked taut, snagging the stick point into the *kōlea*'s throat.

Views

"[A]nd still another way was to catch them in a net. The very best way to catch a large number was with a net fastened to a long stick. A man went in the daytime to look for the place where many plovers were to be found and when he discovered it, he returned there later with the net. When evening came, the plovers flew about and the man imitated the cry of the plover perfectly. The birds then came in large numbers and so he raised his net and caught them all."

(G.W. Kahiolo, Nūpepa Kū'oko'a, *May 9, 1863 trans. M.K. Pukui)*

A legend from long ago tells of a bird hunter named Kumuhana who shamelessly killed *kōlea* even when his stomach was *piha* (full). He was considered inexcusably wasteful by his neighbors. One man in particular, who happened to worship the *kōlea* god Kumukahi, was sickened by the odor of oily smoke coming from Kumuhana's oven. He warned Kumuhana that his disrespect would be fearfully avenged. But the warnings went unheeded. One afternoon a frenzied flock of *kōlea* swirled into Kumuhana's house and picked and pecked and poked and tore him to death. To this day the area in the district of Ka'ū, on the island of Hawai'i, where Kumuhana was killed, is called 'Ai a Kōlea, "Eaten by Kōlea."

Habitat

Kōlea are strongly territorial in feeding and breeding habits. While in Hawai'i, single, often older *kōlea* are commonly seen on the ground in grassy places such as parks, lawns and golf courses. Their designated areas can be roughly traced by the eye when two or more birds share a large field. A *kōlea* generally revisits the same patch of grass each year, and it is possible to become quite familiar with the individual ways of such a returning neigh-

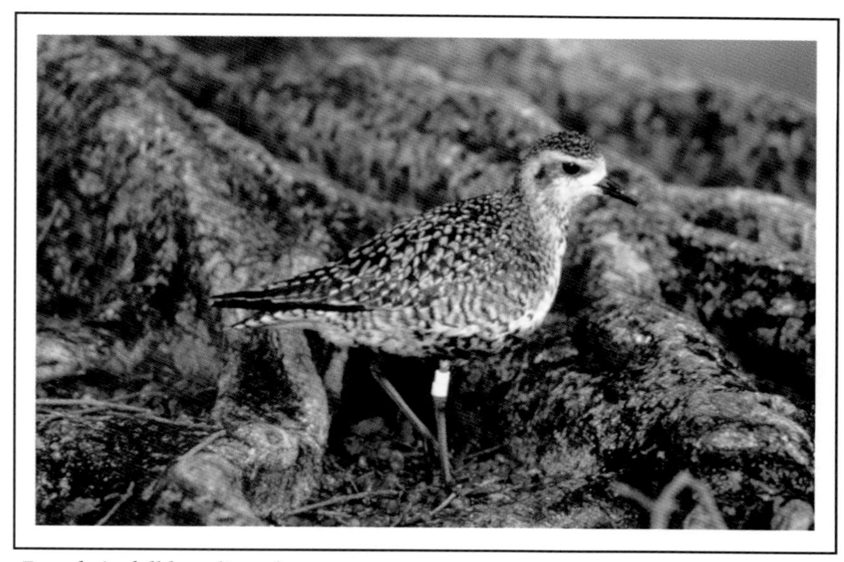

Female in full breeding plumage

Kōlea *gather to migrate.*

bor. Some research suggests that if a returning *kōlea* is denied a customary territory it may starve rather than attempt to enter another *kōlea*'s area, or it may exhaust itself trying to compete with the intruder for the same turf. First-year birds may not find their own territory and end up flocking and sharing a common field. Like a *honu*, which becomes the resident *ʻaumakua* of a particular beach, *kōlea* may live twenty years or more, using the same patch of grass each year. Getting to know a *kōlea* can thus provide a long-term friendship!

The *kōlea* is one of the few native birds that have adapted well to the massive urbanization so destructive of the rural areas that previously provided its feeding grounds. Remarkably, *kōlea*—when in residence from early August to late April—are even seen on the scraps of parks scattered about downtown Honolulu. Their ability to adapt contrasts with that of the *ʻalalā*, which have suffered near extinction from the total impact of humans on their habitat.

Food

As *hoʻoilo* (the wet season) reaches its peak—a time of green grasses in dry places, and a profusion of insects constantly replenishing their numbers in the moist soil—the *kōlea* begin to feed intensely. Day in, day out, with only brief stops for short naps, the leggy *kōlea* zigzag across grassy places: they look, lean, lunge, again and again during their four months of busy feeding. They are building fat reserves that will last the length of the amazing flight they are soon to make, gathering energy for the countless wingbeats that will take them to their faraway nesting sites.

During this time the appearance of the *kōlea* changes noticeably. They grow plump, their feathers shine a rich and fluffy beige-gold and the males slowly take on a handsome tuxedo design. A long stripe, white as tundra snow, appears at the top of the *kōlea* head and runs down the neck and sides. The wing line is outlined in black, and the *kōlea* body glistens with speckles of gold and white.

While in Hawai'i, the *kōlea* often remains a solitary bird, standing alone and alert in a clearly defined territory. Then, at the end of April, near the same date year after year, many suddenly rise up together in great spiraling and whirling flocks, join briefly in a blurry swirl, and vanish northward. It is a sight that few people are lucky to witness.

Just Wondering

***Kōlea** depart Hawai'i at the end of April—often leaving on the same days year after year. Equally punctual is their return flight in early August. Many animals have biological clocks that tick off the timing of their natural rhythms. What other animals in Hawai'i seem to be following their inner clocks? How might these clocks function? How does your biological clockwork work?*

Their destination is the tundra of Alaska and Siberia, some three thousand miles away. When the *kōlea* arrive, nesting sites may still be covered in snow. The *kōlea* rely in part on whatever fat reserves are left after the long flight and eat mostly thawed berries until the snow melts and they can begin to feed again on insects.

Kōlea *eggs blend with their surroundings.*

Reproduction

A simple, almost haphazard nest is assembled on the ground. It typically holds four eggs that are so like their surroundings as to be almost invisible. The nest is about four inches across and lined with leaves and lichens. A similar blotchy color pattern of brown and greenish hues camouflages the eggs. It is a beautiful nest: the eggs, rounded at one end and pointed at the other, come together in a snug fit, like the petals of a flower joined to a center. How easy it is to overlook them or step on them, these warm, smooth ovals that count among evolution's great inventions! The male *kōlea* incubates the eggs during the day, the female by night. Inside the motionless shells the miracle of an egg is again unfolding as amazing change begins to take place.

Within twenty-four hours the single fertilized cell has become millions. A heart is finding first form. On the second day the heart begins to beat, the blood to pump. By the fifth day the *kōlea* is clearly shaped, its eyes bulging, limbs budding. A beak becomes visible at week's end; down appears on the chick's body.

At twelve days a chick is fully shaped within its egg; at twenty days the greater part of the yolk is absorbed. The chick begins to breathe through the tiny holes in the porous shell that allow

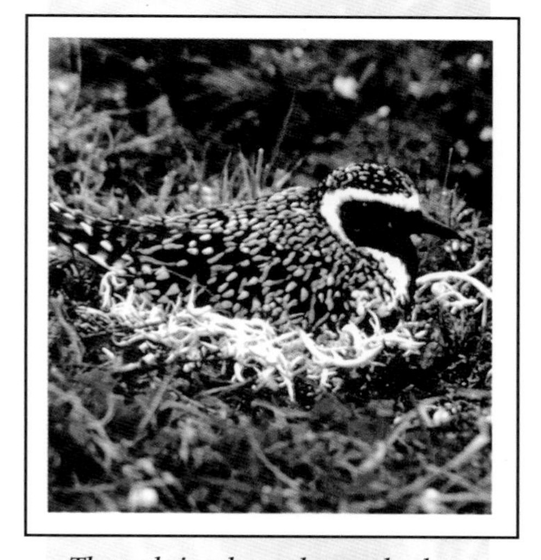

The male incubates the eggs by day.

oxygen to pass in and carbon dioxide to pass out. Shortly before the chick pecks at the shell, cracking its way out, it absorbs the remaining yolk and thus hatches with a full stomach. Because of this it can live up to two days without feeding.

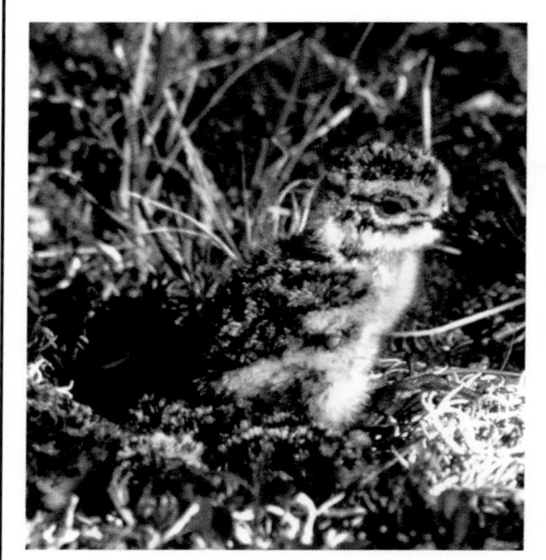

Just Wondering

The egg is truly a miraculous little invention. On a very practical level, it solves many of the problems faced by a land species in assuring its reproduction and survival. As we marvel at the egg, as we stare at the stars and as we feel the force of love in our bodies, can we not wonder—aside from the story of the sperm and the egg: Where does existence come from?

Pecking and pecking away at the inside of the egg, the chick chips a thin strip completely around the shell. It takes six hours or more to free itself and emerge wet and clammy. Born on the ground, the *kōlea* is especially vulnerable, and must not be detected by tundra predators. The fluffy *kōlea*, like ducklings and goslings, hatches with open eyes and a downy body and is capable of leaving the nest almost immediately after hatching.

In about twenty-five days it is bobbing its head and scissoring out its thin young wings to try to fly. The adult *kōlea* return to Hawai'i in early August, leaving their young to grow sturdy another month or two before they set off on the long flight to specks of islands they have never seen.

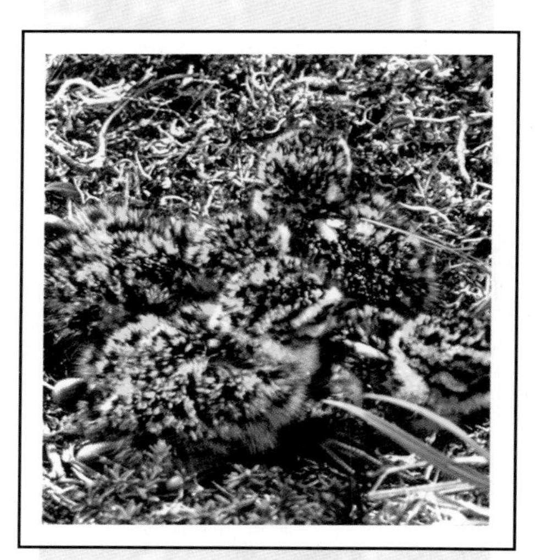

Kōlea *chicks are capable of leaving the nest almost immediately after hatching. Their coloration protects them from detection by predators.*

The development of the young is an astonishingly quick process. An adult *kōlea* is away from Hawai'i only about three and a half months, returning in early August. In these few fleeting weeks, a nest site is chosen, eggs are laid and incubated, and chicks are raised and grow strong enough to undertake the long trip south to faraway islands.

It is not known how the young *kōlea* navigate their way to Hawai'i. How do they get themselves to a land they have never seen? Clearly some marvelous genetic mapping is at work here, perhaps plotting a moonlit, starlit, sunlit course not unlike that which guides turtles, monarch butterflies and other migrating animals to their distant destinations.

It is one of the many mysteries of the world whose solutions await the eager energy of young scientists.

Just Wondering

Hawai'i is a land of many habitats and varied climates. Why should kōlea undertake a hazardous, energy-expensive, three-and-a-half-thousand-mile trip somewhere else, where they lay eggs and raise young, only to return to Hawai'i? Isn't there a suitable place closer to home?

More Kōlea Facts

The *kōlea* often calls out as it takes flight. Hawaiians of old thought they heard in the voice of the *kōlea* a boastful calling out of its own name: *Kōlea ke kōlea I kona inoa iho!* "The *kōlea* '*kōlea*s' its own name!" A braggart is still disapprovingly referred to in Hawaiian as a "*kōlea*."

"Onomatopoeia" is the term used for a word that mimics a sound. "Buzz," "click," "hum," "moo," and "oink" are onomatopoeic words in English. All languages have such special onomatopoeic words. In Hawaiian tradition, the word *kōlea* is thought to be imitative of the sound the plover makes as it takes flight. Eskimo people in Alaska also name the plover by the sound of its call. *Tuusiik* is one Eskimo name for this bird. Another Eskimo group refers to it as *tullik*, the sound their ears hear.

Just Wondering

Do kittens "mew" and cats "meow" everywhere?—or do peoples around the world hear sounds differently?

The famous scientist Charles Darwin once pulled a ball of mud off the feathers of a dead bird and, from the seeds he picked out, succeeded in growing eighty-three plants, representing five different species.

A camouflaged animal's natural coloring or patterning blends with its surroundings, and the animal thus goes undetected. The blotchy brown colors of the *kōlea* egg, for example, so resemble the nest and its surroundings that detection by a hungry predator is difficult. A predator in turn can gain protection from its own camouflage, becoming less visible as it stalks or awaits its prey. Camouflage is a form of mimicry that can include behavior as well as color or pattern. An animal might mimic a particular sound or behavior, protecting itself or its young. The *kōlea* can effectively fake a broken wing, distracting a predator away from its eggs or chicks. Running and thrashing awkwardly with a single wing flapping, the *kōlea* draws the predator away from the nest site, then suddenly flies off to its own safety.

'A'ama *crabs skitter across rocks of identical coloring.*

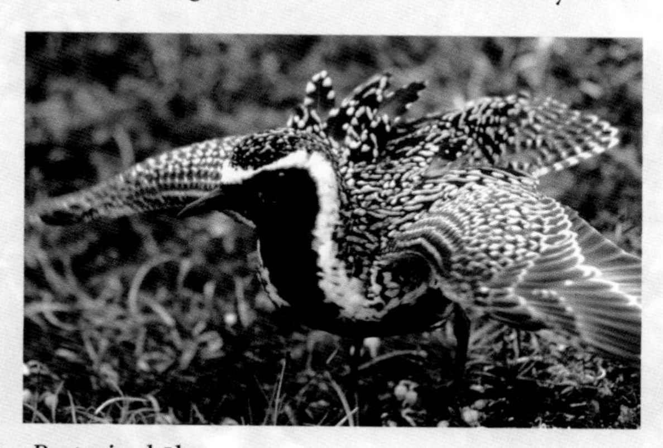

Posturing kōlea

The yolk content of an egg is directly related to the degree of development of the chick when it hatches. An egg that contains only 15 to 20 percent yolk, like those of many perching birds, including the *'alalā*, hatches out a chick that is blind, naked and incapable of faring for itself. The *kōlea* egg contains 52.9 percent yolk, which provides a strong nutritional base for quick development, crucial for a chick born on the ground, needing to fledge and soon to fly thousands of miles over unbroken sea to reach Hawai'i. The nonstop flight of the *kōlea* from Hawai'i to the northern tundra is achieved only because of the huge supply of energy that fuels countless wingbeats. The *kōlea*'s migration path is one of the longest without stopover of any bird. Its flight speed is between sixty and seventy miles per hour at altitudes of up to twenty thousand feet. The trip of three to three-and-a-half thousand miles takes fifty to sixty hours.

Just Wondering

Given that the kōlea weighs no more than a few ounces, its light and quick flight strikes us as perfectly plausible. But what about a 400-ton wide-body commercial airplane, roaring down a runway crammed full of luggage and soda cans, sandwiches and featherless human beings? What exactly gets it up—and keeps it up there?

While much research remains to be done, observers have noted what appear to be three possible behavioral patterns explaining how *kōlea* relate to their territory. Some *kōlea* are entirely solitary. Some feed part of the day near or with others and then go to a specific area. A third group always remains with others of its kind. During migration, solitary birds have been observed leaving the islands first. Having enjoyed their own territories, these birds that do not have to compete for food are fatter and faster. At their departure, other *kōlea* move into the available areas, fatten up, and take off at a later date.

Just Wondering

"How do they figure out who owns what? What's the procedure for dividing up a golf course? Or a graveyard? There must be a zillion golden plover plots within the city limits that the land office never heard of. It's an underground real estate operation that boggles the mind."

(Bob Krauss, Honolulu Advertiser, *August 25, 1999)*

If you've flown a model airplane, you know how the fuel tank relates to the intense whirling of the propeller. Likewise, if there is to be sufficient energy for flight, a small bird must eat constantly, each day consuming about one-third of its body weight in food. In human terms, a youth weighing one hundred pounds would have to eat more than thirty pounds of food daily to match a bird's intake. The *kōlea* needs a store of reserve energy in its fatty tissues to make the long flight and sustain itself if the northern summer is late.

Hawaiian Settlement: Human Intrusions

Voyages: Slicing the Glimmering Sea

At first stars steered them, currents and birds led them and winds leaned on their sails, but in the final dark hours of dawn, it was the fragrant scent of land that drew the canoes to the land. As the slim vessels rose and fell, slicing the glimmering morning sea, and the land loomed high, a single voice stirred the silence with chant: *Eia Hawai'i, he moku, he kanaka.* The words proclaimed a naming of the land and the arrival of humans to Hawai'i.

The Polynesian discovery of these remote islands was a remarkable feat of skill and faith, courage and grand adventure. Men and women on bold voyaging canoes, like the first plant and animal colonizers, depended as well on wind and wave to find their way to the dots of land they would call Hawai'i.

Petroglyph: Glazed stone sail billows off a sea of lava.

Views

"We probably once had the innate ability to orient ourselves on the earth, but we've lost it. Now learning the navigation skills of the Polynesians means rediscovering our inborn capacities. Look at what the animals know—whales, sea turtles, birds and insects—sometimes traveling thousands of miles to tiny islands to breed. If they're not precise they'll die. Of course the navigator uses techniques and bits of information accumulated over years of ocean experience, but he must also relearn the capacity to be fully attuned to his environment, fully concentrated on what's going on around him. He relies on the five physical senses, and a sixth, spiritual, one as well."

(Master navigator Nainoa Thompson, in E. Herter, 1993)

Just Wondering

It is said that ancient inhabitants of North America were so close to nature that they could see stars during daylight hours. Pacific Islanders were also thought to have extraordinary navigational skills that helped in their great oceanic migrations. Nainoa often tells of a time when he and his teacher, Mau Piailug, stood in the evening light at Lāna'i Point Lookout on O'ahu. Gazing out to sea, Mau quietly asked Nainoa: "Where is Tahiti?" With a moment's consideration, Nainoa pointed "There!" Then, after some silence, Mau asked: "And can you see it?"

INTENTIONAL INTRODUCTIONS: FOR FOOD AND FIBER

On deck, pressed in netted calabashes, *moa* (jungle fowl) clucked and crowed;

Morning landing: the voyaging canoe Hōkūle'a *approaches a smoking, steaming coast where magma meets sea.*

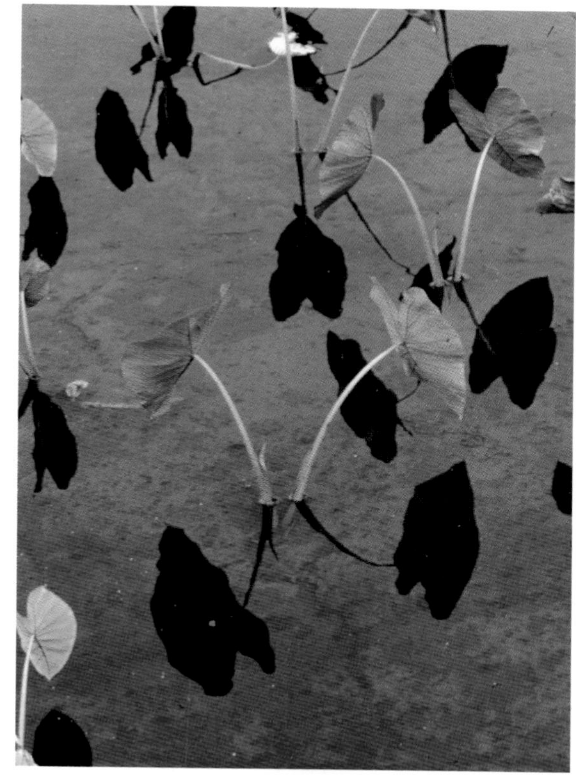

Young, well-spaced taro. All parts of the plant are eaten.

bristly *pua'a* (pigs) fettered in branch cages, grunted and squealed; small, barkless *'īlio* (dogs) yapped weakly, wagging tails in excitement.

Canoe cargo held provisions of a people intent on settling unknown land, people bringing with them the plants they were accustomed to for food, fiber and medicine: breadfruit and mountain apple saplings, banana shoots and sugarcane slips, cuttings of sweet potato and stalks of taro, coconuts and a variety of medicinal plants. All of these plants and animals were purposely packed onboard the voyaging canoes to feed, clothe and heal settlers on an unknown land. They are the first examples of intentional introductions by humans to the Hawaiian Islands. It is now thought that once Polynesians had discovered these new islands, occasional voyages were made to and from the Society and Marquesas islands in central East Polynesia, and perhaps even beyond to the Tuamotu Archipelago and the Cook Islands. Over time, as many as twenty-six plants were intentionally brought to Hawai'i during these crossings.

Unintentional Introductions: Brown Rats, Black Flies

Polynesian canoes also carried uninvited guests. Concealed between dark deck planks, in folded *kapa* mats and the soil pouches of plants, were skinks, geckos, rats, and a variety of seeds, snails and insects. Pesky flies buzzed about, annoying animals and people alike; head lice crept on itchy human scalps. All of these plants and animals—both the intentional and unintentional introductions—were new to Hawai'i. They would alter the *'āina* (land) in significant ways, and the land would be forever changed.

Moa *(jungle fowl)*

Mature taro and ancient mountains, Kauaʻi

Hawaiians Settle: Using the Land

When Hawaiians first arrived—probably in A.D. 0 to 800—they settled along the coasts. Hunting and gathering, lowland agriculture, and the sea sustained most of their needs. In prehuman times, inland forests are thought to have stretched down to the very seashore. As planters, Hawaiians fire-cleared lowlands to build housesites and grow their introduced crops. It was the cultivation of *kalo* (taro) that set many basic patterns of their culture: the way water was regulated and where houses came to be located; the festivals and rituals in honor of the gods; the daily eating habits of commoners as well as chiefs. Native planters became skilled as engineers and builders of *loʻi kalo* (taro terraces), which were joined by intricate networks of irrigation gutters. Many of these little canals have held to this day and can be seen still running stony water through the backyards of such residential areas as Nuʻuanu, *ma uka* of Honolulu.

The exceptional engineering skills of Hawaiians were also apparent in the walls they built. Large rocks, locked lengthwise into walls, provided the near-indestructible strength of steel rebar rods running through modern-day concrete. Remarkably,

Water sparkles and rolls on a taro leaf.

in places where powerful earthquakes commonly shake the land, many of these old walls still stand strong today.

Hawaiians developed a rich knowledge of the cultivation of different plants, especially notable in the development of new varieties. As many as three hundred different kinds of *kalo* were cultivated by Hawaiian farmers, distinct varieties adapted to the different conditions of this land's weather, water and soil. Numerous types of sweet potatoes and gourds were also developed. Hand pollination to increase crop yield was one remarkable agricultural practice of old Hawai'i:

Views

"As we went through the streets of Honoruru [Honolulu], we noticed at almost all the open places and near the houses, a great quantity of Argemone mexicana*, which grows everywhere as a weed. We noticed an Indian [Hawaiian] woman standing in the midst of some of these plants, taking hold of flowers and using them for something; we went up to her and saw to our astonishment that she was cleverly spreading the pollen of a blossom upon its stigma. On our asking why she was doing it, she answered that it would make more seed grains come forth, which are used for eating there like we use our poppies. It would be interesting to know, yet not easily proved, whether the inhabitants of the Sandwich Islands had an anticipation of the different species of plants earlier than Europeans."*

(F.J.F. Meyen, 1834, trans. W.D. Alexander)

The Land Changes: Fire to Food

Lowland environments were greatly affected by all human activities. It is thought that the scorching off of trees, bushes and grasses caused the disappearance of much of the lowland insect and snail life that had evolved in this dry-forest habitat over thousands of years. Pigs, rats, lizards and dogs were all new to the land. They moved into habitats that had never before known serious competition, and their numbers probably increased quickly.

Pressing, pounding the taro produces a smooth and lump-free poi.

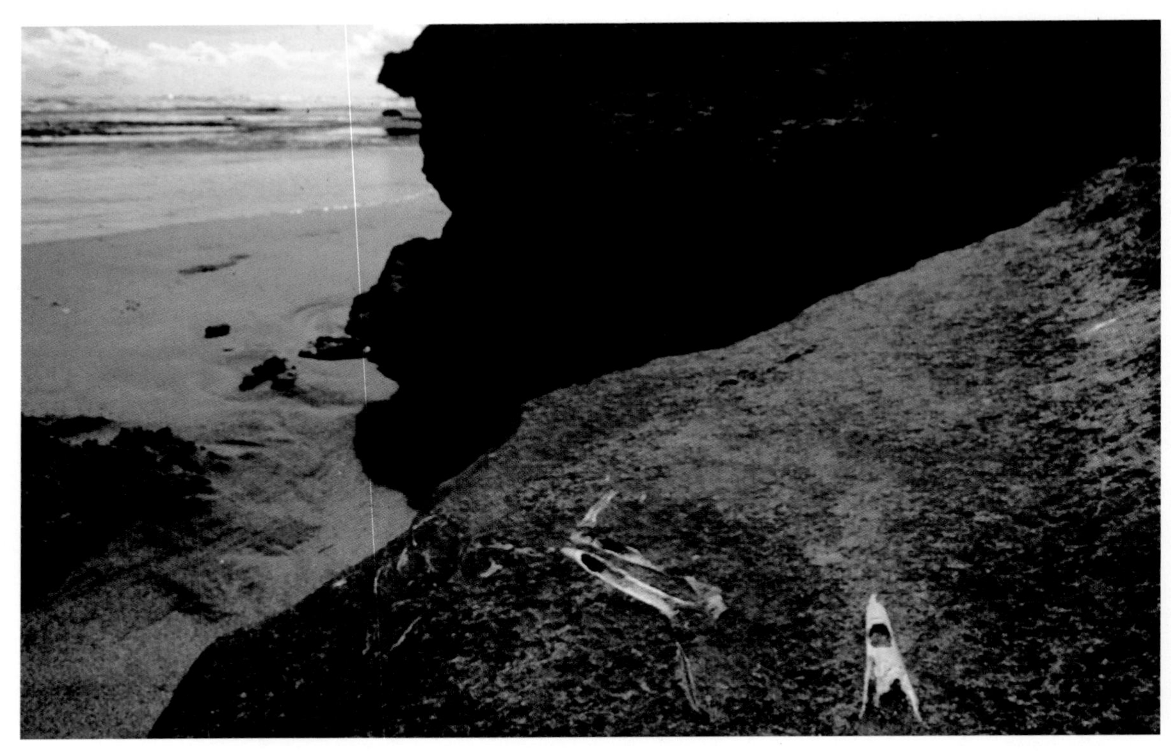

Erosion exposes bones of a long-extinct flightless Hawaiian bird: Kaua'i

Archeological digs suggest that bird extinctions may have occurred before the arrival of humans to Hawai'i, but during the early period of Hawaiian settlement the impact on endemic birds was probably significant. Flightless birds were easily caught and consumed: joyous feasting was surely one of the many pleasures this new land offered the first generations of Hawaiian families. At least sixty species, including two types of flightless ibis, eight species of flightless geese, a bird-eating hawk, an eagle, three long-legged owls, seven flightless rails and two species of crows are thought to have disappeared after Hawaiians arrived. Like humans today, so many of whom go about their lives unaware of the impact they are having on the environment and the consequences on native species, Hawaiians of old probably did not realize until much later the full extent of the changes and how the land was being affected.

At the same time, it is likely that new kinds of environments were created, promoting the well-being of other species. As streams were dammed and diverted, drying out lowland wetlands and creating new irrigated areas for the planting of taro, Hawaiians may have created ideal habitats for ducks and other water birds that had not previously established or grown abundant.

Along the shore, shallow bays were ringed with long strands of rocks and stocked with fish, creating advanced forms of fish production and giving the coastal landscape a sheltered beauty. Writing in 1868, Hawaiian author Samuel Kamakau stated that "Fishponds were things that beautified the land, and a land with many fishponds was called 'fat.' "

Fishpond walls were built curved: currents passed ponds in a rounded flow, carrying off sand and debris that could clog inside waters. Seaside rocks angled downward into the base: crashing waves over time pushed them to a tighter lock. Walls thus withstood centuries of slamming storm waves.

With reefs edging up several hundred yards offshore, the islands of Kaua'i, O'ahu and Moloka'i were best suited for fishponds. O'ahu, considered one of the most beautiful of the islands by the people of old, had nearly half the 350 or more fishponds looping along the shores of the Hawaiian Islands and was considered highly desirable when chiefs made war to acquire new land.

The southern coast of Moloka'i was also famous for its fishponds, several of which are being restored today. These ponds are unique examples of Hawaiians' engineering skills and understanding of the complexity and interrelatedness of natural habitats. Elaborate systems designed in prehistoric times to utilize the in- and outflow of tides for the stocking of fish and the creation of a rich nutrient base to assure rapid fish growth are employed to this day in modern aquaculture projects throughout the islands. Kamakau, quoted above, noted the wonderful abundance of food provided so conveniently by such coastal ponds:

Views

"[On the nights of high tide] the keeper would dip his foot into the water at the mākāhā *[sea opening], and if the sea pressed in like a stream and felt warm, then he knew that the sluice would be full of fish. The fish would scent the fresh sea and long for it. I have seen them become like wild things. At a sluice where the fish had been treated like pet pigs, they would crowd to the* mākāhā, *where the keepers felt them with their hands and took whatever of them they wanted, perhaps* awa, 'anae, 'ō'io, *or whatever they desired.*

(S. Kamakau, trans. M.K. Pukui, 1976)

Kaua'i fishpond. A normally socked-in Hā'upu Mountain looms high and clear.

Preserving the Land: A Fragile, Vulnerable Place

High mountain habitats, called *wao akua* (forest of the gods), were probably little changed by human activities. Hawaiians believed that forest attracted water to the land: *Hahai nō ka ua i ka ululāʻau,* "The rain follows the forest." Perhaps in part for this reason the far uplands were little used. *Koa*, the majestic tree previously unknown to Polynesians, was logged from high forests and lugged to shore for carving canoes; feathers were plucked off native birds to craft beautiful royal capes; stone adzes were chipped sharp at quarries located

Basket and gourd containers

Hala *leaves for plaiting*

high on the chilly cinder cones of Mauna Kea. In all likelihood, Hawaiians entered and left the misty highlands in ways that little affected this pristine ecosystem and its many species found nowhere else on Earth.

The people of old both revered and modified their environment. Dramatic disruptions did occur, particularly in lowland habitats. But Hawaiians, like island people everywhere, surely came to view their *ʻāina* as a precious and limited

The past meets the future: ancient cultural habits of poi *eating and* hala *plaiting together with introduced cat, saw and bottle.*

Gazing skyward in a grove of twilight palms

resource, one to be used and preserved. For centuries before the arrival of Westerners, perhaps because Hawaiians had come to understand the *ʻāina* as a fragile, vulnerable place, the use of the land was regulated by a strict code called the *kapu* system, which determined how and when resources could be used. Kamehameha the Great is reported to have said: "The feathers belong to me, but the birds themselves belong to my heirs."

Over time a new balance was established as introduced Polynesian species, including humans, adapted to the land and the land adjusted to them. Early foreign visitors, writing about Waikīkī, Oʻahu, described a settled, highly regulated, and beautiful landscape:

Views

"The verge of the shore was planted with a large grove of coconut palms, affording a delightful shade to the scattered habitations of the natives. . . . We pursued a pleasing path back into the plantation, which was nearly level and very extensive, and laid out with great neatness into little fields, planted with taro, yams, sweet potatoes, and the cloth plant. These, in many cases, were divided by little banks on which grew the sugar cane and a species of Draecena *without the aid of much cultivation, and the whole was watered in a most ingenious manner by dividing the general stream into little aqueducts leading in various directions so as to supply the most distant fields at pleasure, and the soil seems to repay the labor and industry of these people by the luxuriancy of its production."*

(A. Menzies, naturalist and surgeon, H.M.S. Discovery, *1792)*

Views

"He [Captain Douglas] was received very cordially by Titeeree [Kahekili] who took him round the village, showed him several plantations, and conducted him to some large ponds, which appeared to be full of fish. He mentioned also some others where he had a quantity of turtle."

(John Meares, "Extracts from Voyages Made in the Years 1788 and 1789," Hawaiian Historical Society Reprints 1)

Just Wondering

Would a modern-day kapu *system be a culturally appropriate way to deal with the serious decline in near-shore and offshore fish populations?*

Good Friend, Good Food

The Dog

Lore and Legend

According to one Polynesian legend, the first dog was created when Māui, famous demigod, trickster, and snarer of the sun, in a fit of fury crushed his brother-in-law Irawaru beneath the outrigger of their fishing canoe. While they were at sea, the fish had gone only to Irawaru's hooks, and Māui's shame boiled to a beastly rage. Moody, scheming trickster that he was, Māui plotted his chance for revenge. When the canoe was safely beached, he suddenly heaved down on the outrigger with such force that the brother's body flattened and lengthened to a long, tail-tipped dog form. Māui then changed his brother's voice to a yapping yowl, and so it was that the first dog took shape.

Mythical dogs roamed many a valley in old Hawai'i, sometimes changing to *mo'o* (lizards) to slide into mountain streams and hide. One of the most famous of these dogs is the small white companion of the goddess Pele, occasionally seen with her as she crosses the craggy lava fields of Kīlauea. Before settling on the island of Hawai'i, Pele had spent time on Kaua'i, O'ahu and then Maui—as long as their volcanic activity still pleased her. But these islands grew older and colder, and when O'ahu's volcanic fires began to fail, Pele left in search of a hotter home, a trek that finally took her to Halema'uma'u caldera on the Big Island. While on O'ahu, Pele had kept friends and demigods along the windward coast, one of whom remains fixed in rock on the bluff bending into beautiful Kahana Bay. Now known mistakenly as "The Crouching Lion," its true and ancient identity as a dog is unfortunately unknown to today's gazing tourists.

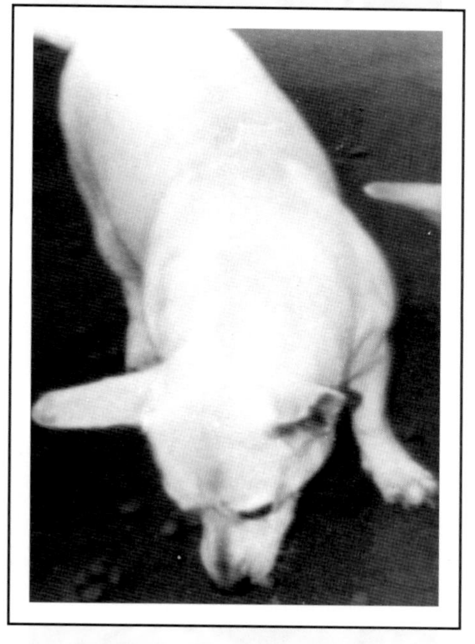

Hawaiian Name: *'Īlio*
Scientific Name: *Canis familiaris*
Area of Origin: Southeast Asia
Date of Arrival:
Prehistoric, probable Polynesian import

Just Wondering

How does the ancient story of Pele's wanderings match up with a present-day geological explanation of the creation of the Hawaiian chain?

Polynesian dogs were small, long-backed, stubby-legged animals of short, brush-bristle fur and small, upright ears. An old Hawaiian woman whose name has been lost in time assured a traveler to the islands in the 1830s that hanging ears were considered the sign of an inferior dog. Big and gentle eyes and sluggish dispositions made these little dogs beloved pets and easy travelers onboard cramped, slender-hulled sailing canoes traveling the distance to and from Hawai'i. Perhaps because of Māui's vengeful trick, Hawaiian dogs never barked, but instead yapped.

Dogs were favored pets as well as prized food in old Hawai'i. Archaeologists have uncovered dog bones wrapped in *kapa* and placed close by the remains of what is assumed to be their master. A puppy and baby were sometimes nursed together, sharing the *mana* of the mother and creating a strong bond between them, which carried into childhood. At the death of the dog, one of its teeth was worn by the child as a neck charm against sorcery. If the child died before the dog, the pet was killed and wrapped in the *kapa* bundle next to the body of the child.

If a dog prowled about and howled in ancient times, or just growled aimlessly, it was believed that the spirit of a dead or dying person had drifted near. A dog digging a hole near a house was also thought to be the sign of death approaching. The hole had to be filled immediately!

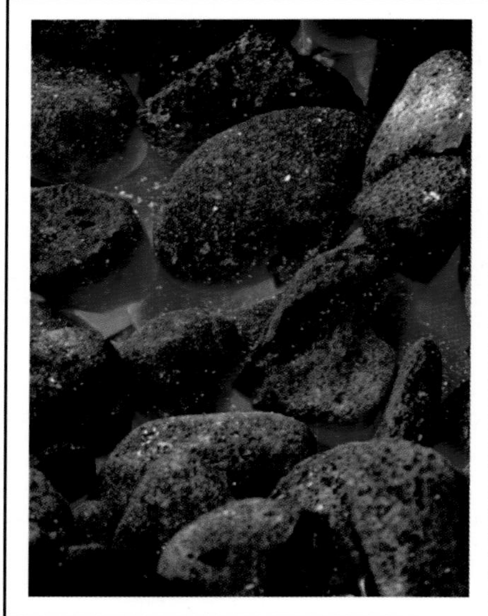

Firing up imu *stones*

Habitat

Both pigs and dogs were herded together near housesites, either penned or free-ranging. During the period of early Hawaiian settlement, neither animal is thought to have gone wild and taken to roaming the highlands in significant numbers.

Dog was a delicious part of the Hawaiian diet, more highly esteemed than pig or chicken, and often reserved for *ali'i*. In ancient times the plumpest dogs were collected for the chiefs' feasting. Dogs being fattened for eating were held in small pens and fed with taro root mashed with broth for the delicate flavor and tenderness it gave their flesh. For this reason they came to be called "*poi* dogs." Puppies were finger-fed *poi* several times a day and given sweet potatoes and other vegetables until their backs broadened.

Dogs were killed by strangulation, and the blood was poured into a gourd. Clean, hot pebbles were dropped in to simmer the blood to thickness. The body hair was rubbed off and the puppy was rinsed, flattened and salted, then broiled over coals or hot rocks. Big dogs were cooked in the *imu* (underground oven) in the same way as pigs. Hot rocks were tucked into the body cavity;

it was wrapped with ti or banana leaves, more hot stones were added, and the pit was covered with earth, sealing in the leaf-scented, steaming heat.

Reproduction

The *poi* dog bore and birthed puppies like female dogs everywhere. Dogs can mate and bear twice a year, as was surely encouraged in ancient times, given the Hawaiian fondness for this tasty food.

Nine weeks is the time it takes for the female to carry her puppies to birth. Shortly before the young arrive, she gathers together a nest. In days past, the female probably assembled leaves and perhaps pieces of old *kapa* in a sheltered spot where she could birth alone.

Each pup emerges wrapped in a shiny, cellophane-like pouch, which the female must quickly tear away so that the puppy can breathe. She eats the membrane and licks the puppy clean. The licking stimulates blood flow and activates vital organs—not the least important those that enable to the pup to pee and poop. Without this stimulation, it will die. The female has at most eight minutes to release each puppy from its enveloping sack before it dies of suffocation.

With warmth and nursing and continuous care, the blind, chubby *poi* puppies soon open their eyes and wobble and hobble out into the world to begin their adorable, romping rambunctiousness.

The Hawaiian *poi* dog would be forever changed by the arrival of Westerners. Like so many native plants and animals, its encounter with the West meant disaster that would ultimately mark its disappearance as a distinct breed. Our great grandparents still told stories of having seen one or another of the last of the old *poi* dogs. Apparently, in contact with European breeds, the *poi* dog quickly learned to bark. As it began interbreeding, its flesh also lost the delicate sweet flavor and succulence that made it a preferred food of the people of old. Mixed-breed mongrel strays became street scavengers and a considerable nuisance to Honolulu residents, or drifted off to hills and valleys where they banded in packs of marauding wild dogs.

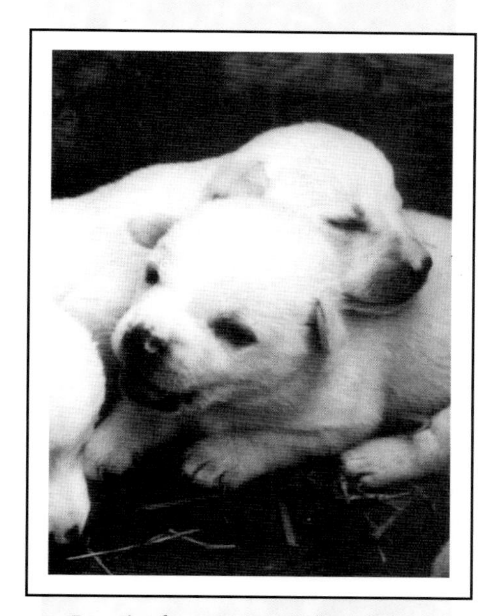

Puppies from 1967 poi *dog project at Honolulu Zoo*

Views

"What a perfect nuisance are those abominable, beastly imitations of the canine species, which infest our village; such a rawboned, skinny, wilted looking assortment of ghosts ought to be banished from our society in these reformed times. It takes three of them to raise a growl, and six to bark, and then each yelping cur is obliged to lean against a fence to rest."

(Stephen D. Mackintosh, Sandwich Island Gazette, *May 12, 1838)*

More Dog Facts

Māui's role as creator of the first dog is told in earlier myths of other Pacific peoples. In each version, it is always Māui's vengeful anger that causes him to turn the perceived troublemaker into a dog. In one memorable tale, Māui persuades his brother-in-law to lie still, quietly delouses him, and then, with the help of a powerful spell, stretches him into a dog that whimpers and scampers about on all fours.

Hawaiians had little understanding of the *haole*'s disdain for dog yet delight in hog. To the Hawaiian mind both made fine pets and fine meals and one should not rule out the other. It soon became evident that the *haole* prejudice in this area lay more in the mind then in the taste buds. One rather uppity missionary wife, Lucy Thurston, recorded the following prank in 1820:

Views

"Natives consider baked dog a great delicacy, too much so in the days of their idolatry ever to allow it to pass the lips of women. They never offer it to foreigners, who hold it in great abhorrence. Once they mischievously attached a pig's head to a dog's body, and thus inveigled a foreigner to partake of it to his great acceptance."

(In M. Titcomb, 1969)

"Man's best friend" has at times been heroically loyal to a master. On February 19, 1857, the *Pacific Commercial Advertiser* reported that Evelaina, the favorite dog of Kamehameha III, would not leave her master's grave following his death. When food and water were no longer provided the dog, hunger and thirst drove her off, but she returned again and again. For more than two years she kept graveside watch, until the day she suddenly disappeared and was never seen again.

NO KA ILIO.

"Auhea oukou e na lii a me ka poe i kohoia iloko o ka ahaolelo; e ola a me ka pomaikai oukou, a me ke aupuni.

Eia kekahi mea, manao makou e hoopii aku imua o oukou a na oukou e noonoo a imi i ka pono a me ka hewa o ko makou manao. I ko makou ike ana he mea ino ka ilio o Hawaii nei, a pomaikai ke aupuni ke imi iho a pau loa paha. Eia na hewa a makou i ike ai ma na ilio.

I. He mea pelapela ka ilio; ua pili ka uku ia ia, a me ka lepo, a i kona noho ana iloko o ka hale, ua pelapela ka hale ia ia, a he mea ia e ino ai ka noho ana o na kanaka.

II. Eia kekahi; he hoaai, he hoamoe, he hoahele, he hoalauna ka ilio no na kanaka o Hawaii nei. Malama nui kekahi poe wahine i ka ilio, aole malama i kana keiki; he aloha i ka ilio a halihali ia ia iloko o kona poli a waiho wale i ke keiki me ke aloha ole.

III. O ka ilio kekahi mea e ilihune ai na kanaka. Nui ka ai i pau ia ia; nui na moa, na pelehu, na koloa, na kao a me na hipa i pau ia ia i ka aihue, a nolaila kekahi ilihune.

IV. Eia kekahi: he nui ka waiwai i lilo no ka ilio, a he hapa loa ka waiwai i loaa hou mai ia ia. Aole i like me kekahi mau holoholona, e like me ka hipa, ko kao, ka bipi, ka puaa, a me na manu; he mau holoholona keia e waiwai ai na kanaka. Aole loa pela ka ilio, he mea ia e ilihune ai.

V. Eia kekahi ino o ka ilio, o ka hae wale aku i ke kanaka ma ke alanui e hele ana: a nahu wale hoi kekahi poe ilio i na keiki a me na kanaka.

VI. Aole pono e malama i ka ilio i *mea ai*; aole ai na kanaka naauao i ka ilio, hoopailua loa lakou ia mea ino. Ma na aina naaupo wale no, ai na kanaka i ka ilio. He mea hilahila keia.

VII. Ua pili kekahi mai i ka ilio, a ina noho pu kela ilio mai me na kamalii, lele ka mai meeau maluna o na keiki, a poino lakou.

E na lii a me ka poe i kohoia, pehea ko oukou manao i keia mau hewa o na ilio? Aole anei he oiaio? Ina he oiaio, ea, e kau mai oukou i kanawai no ka ilio i emi iho a anea-ne pau loa lakou. Penei paha ka pono, *e auhau i na ilio a pau i hapawalu no ka makahiki no kela ilio keia ilio.* Alaila paha makau na kanaka i keia auhau a hoopau i na ilio. Ina he ilio maikai, he kiai no ka hale, e ola paha ia a oluolu kona haku i ka uku i hapawalu nona. Aia no nae i ko oukou manao.

Na inoa — Na inoa

Hawaiian language poster from late 1800s describes dogs as dirty, flea-ridden animals that steal poultry, transmit diseases and harass passers-by.

Occasionally, you still might notice a small dog walking along a street and you feel sure it's a *poi* dog. The traits are all there: the bowlegged gait, curved-up tail, pointed muzzle and upright ears. After a hundred and more years the blood is still around, however diluted by generations of dog interbreedings. In 1967, the Honolulu Zoo attempted through selective breeding to recreate the little Polynesian dog. Two dogs of a wild New Guinea species, said to be distant ancestors of the Polynesian dog, were brought in and several little mutts with strong *poi* dog features were located in South Kona. Results were very promising and the project was considered quite a success until it lost its funding.

One of thousands of stray mongrels that once roamed Hawai'i's streets and hills

Views

"We have a kennel of 19 now but it will be a good five years more before we achieve similar characteristics found in skeletons or early drawings. We've got to unteach him to bark. Barking is learned and inherited but practice is important."

(Jack Throp, former director, Honolulu Zoo, quoted in Honolulu Magazine, *December, 1969)*

Just Wondering

How does a dog practice unbarking?

Wild dogs were a serious problem on many of the islands until quite recently. On O'ahu in the mid-1950s, it was estimated that over five hundred dogs still roamed hills and valleys, running in packs, harassing hikers, raiding chicken farms and killing small cows. In 1955, seventeen calves were killed in dog raids on two herds in Wai'anae. On two occasions that year humans were attacked. The last goat to live on Diamond Head held off two wild dogs in a bloody skirmish that lasted most of a day in August, 1955, and made front page news the next morning. It seems the billy came out the winner, for he was seen clambering along the cliffs above the lighthouse some years afterward.

A dog's nose has 200 million smell receptor cells; a human nose has 5 million. The dog can distinguish hundreds of separate smells with a single whiff and from that tangle, sort out one scent "thread" and follow it to its source.

Just Wondering

What does the world look like to a dog?

Hawaiian Name: *Mo'o 'alā*
Area of origin:
Southeast Asia
Date of Arrival:
Probable Polynesian import; other species introduced at later time

Camouflage and Detachable Tails

The Gecko

Arrival in Hawai'i

Canoes coming to Hawai'i carried their hidden cargo of stowaways: geckos and skinks concealed in crevices where sturdy bark cordage belted beams tight; small rats in dark places in deck planks; insects and weeds packed in pouches of soil bound around each plant.

Lore and Legend

In old Hawai'i the little *mo'o* that warmed themselves on sunny rocks and sped up thatched walls in pursuit of insects were always shown great respect. A person who broke a *mo'o* egg might be severely punished by falling off a *pali.*

In some families, the *mo'o* was an important *'aumakua*; in other families, *'aumākua* appeared as owls or sharks. While the great god Kanaloa breathed in and out the daily tides on Hawaiian beaches, it was the *'aumākua* such as the *honu* or *manō* (shark) that Hawaiians called on for protection in times of need at sea.

The legendary *mo'o* that guarded ponds was not the friendly, slight gecko or skink that we know today, but rather a slow, often fearful creature, a low and dark shape that lay lurking in a mountain pool. The yellowing of leaves on trees and shrubs near the pool, a yellowish taint to the water below, or scummy foam floating on the pool surface were sure and scary signs that a *mo'o* was there.

Views

"The mo'o had extremely long and terrifying bodies. . . . They were not seen just at any time, but when the fires were lighted on the ko'a *altars beside their homes. There was no doubting them when they were seen. . . . When given a drink of* 'awa *they would turn from side to side like the hull of a canoe in the water."*

(S. Kamakau, trans. M.K. Pukui, 1976)

Mo'o could also show a protective and helpful side. Hauwahine, a *mo'o* that lived in Kawainui and Ka'elepulu on O'ahu, was both feared and loved, as she sheltered her people from bad chiefs and kept these areas fertile.

Geckos probably got their English name from a Malay word that, by its sound, imitates the slurpy chirp-chirp of the gecko. This noise is made by the gecko's tongue clicking against the roof of its mouth. Geckos are unique among lizards in that they have a voice. They also have excellent hearing. Eyelids, however, are fused open: in several species, a long pink tongue can curl up over the cheek and wipe the eyeball moist and clean.

When grasped by a predator, a gecko tail may detach and lie wriggling vigorously for several minutes. In a form of mimicry not unlike the behavior of the *kōlea* when it fakes a broken wing to divert a predator, the thrashing tail momentarily distracts the attacker, and the gecko scoots to safety. In time, a new tail grows out, though it might stay stunted or crooked. Occasionally, two tails sprout out. As a survival skill, the trick seems to work: detached tails are frequently found in the stomachs of a wide variety of predators. Some species of geckos, when pinned down by a predator, can quickly shed their skin, causing the attacker to lose its clutch; a speedy gecko can escape. Camouflage also may fool predators. When sitting on a light background, some geckos become so pale that only beady eyes reveal their whereabouts. On a piece of bark or a dark wall, gecko color darkens rapidly.

Today, there are at least five species of nocturnal geckos in Hawaiʻi, two of which—the house gecko and the mourning gecko—commonly inhabit our homes. The mourning gecko is one of several species that probably came with the original Polynesian settlers, but is now relatively uncommon in many areas as the more aggressive house gecko expands its range. The feisty house gecko arrived in Hawaiʻi in the 1940s, probably as a stowaway on military transport during the war. All five species originated in Southeast Asia and in general have similar habits.

Habitat

While other species of geckos occur on the barks and rocks of field and wood, the common house gecko has long lived in close association with human beings. In our homes they gather at *lānai* (porch) lights to gorge on moths and termites. They chirp curtly, curl tails angrily, and chase each other along the ceiling line of walls.

Geckos on a screen, waiting for bugs

Food

Geckos feed on insects and are important helpers in keeping pest populations in check, particularly in our homes. Like cats, geckos usually pounce only when a prey moves. They are wonderfully adept at overtaking a moving bug, shooting straight up walls, scooting right across ceilings upside down—not with the help of Scotch tape soles or suction cups on their scaled toes, but rather by inserting tiny bristle toe-hooks into the minute crevices found on any surface, including bathroom tiles and glass. Individual scales have hundreds of hairlike bristles, each of which in turn is covered with as many as two thousand tiny hairs. Together, they

provide countless hooks that hold onto the surface through a complicated process of molecular forces. The result is a sure-footed Velcro cling. Occasionally, a gecko will drop with the plop of a belly flop to the floor. This is usually the outcome of skirmishing over territory with an aggressive neighbor, causing one of the geckos to lose toehold.

Geckos enjoy an occasional change of diet. Once accustomed to their human surroundings, they become quite bold, at times climbing right up on a kitchen table, where they have been seen casually licking guava jelly off a breakfast knife or lapping up a drop of dripped honey.

Gecko Reproduction

Two types of geckos in Hawai'i are parthenogenic. Each lizard is female, and eggs develop without fertilization by a male. The female house gecko does, however, mate with a male, at which point his contribution to assuring the next generation of geckos is over.

The female holds her paired eggs within her for a period before placing them in a protected, sunless spot. Often, as she waddles her way up the outside of a window pane, twin lumpy eggs show through the skin of her bumpy belly.

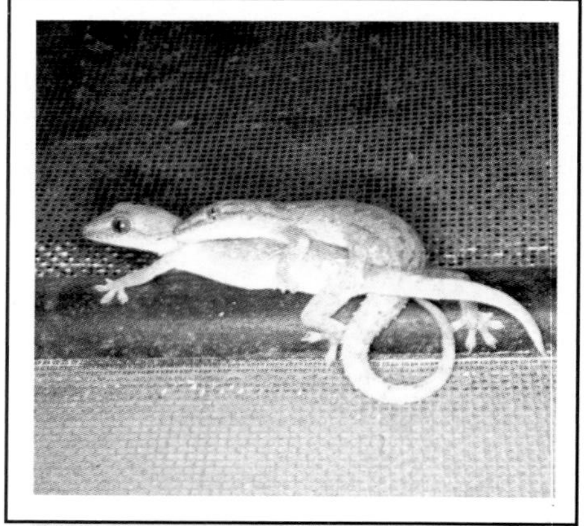

Geckos mating

Geckos cluster their porcelain eggs in any dark crack or crevice. The eggs, when first laid, are moist and adhesive. Usually laid two at a time, they instantly bond to each other and glue to the surface on which they have been placed by the female. A favored site may be visited by many females until a score or more little eggs are lined up in clustered strands. Air turns the shell brittle, molding it to the surface on which it is attached. This often causes one side of the egg to harden flat.

Depending on the weather, eggs hatch in three to four weeks. The baby gecko's oversized head has a set of sharp egg teeth at the tip of its snout. These are used for breaking out by pricking the crisp shell wall. Soon after hatching, the tiny teeth drop away and the gecko gains the strength it needs to skitter off for a first meal. The gecko's skin sheds several times in the coming weeks. As the skin flakes and peels along the body, the lizard turns and tears it off, devouring it in strained gulps.

Gecko eggs

Just Wondering

What's Mother Nature up to here that leads the gecko to munch on itself in such a wonderful example of self-recycling?

More Gecko Facts

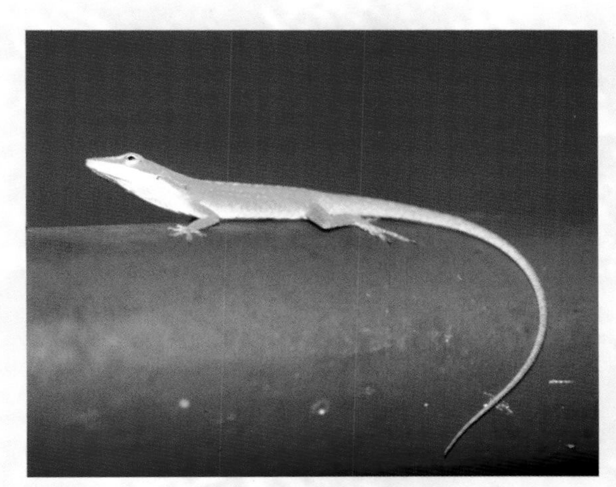

Anole lizard, or chameleon

A *mo'o* that is now very familiar on O'ahu is the anole lizard, native to Cuba and locally referred to as a chameleon for its remarkable ability to change color from bright lime green to olive brown. Quite tame, the anole is common in our gardens, quietly basking in the sun and easily caught by hand. The male is recognizable by the reddish orange flap beneath his neck, which he inflates with jerks of his head, exaggerating his size and posturing up a territorial claim. The anole was most likely a pet release and was first seen in the Kaimukī area of Honolulu in 1950. It has thrived in Hawai'i, probably because it is a day feeder, stalking insects in a niche previously unoccupied. The anole chameleon uses its eyes and color detectors in its skin in adjusting to its background. Messages from its brain travel as chemicals in the bloodstream, causing a change of pigmentation in its cells. This process of color change occurs gradually in the chameleon and the gecko. In other animals, such as the squid or octopus, messages rush quickly along nerves, and color changes occur almost instantly.

Just Wondering

By changing their colors, octopuses can communicate irritation with a rival as well as attraction to a mate. The colors of flowers bring pollinators, while color in some butterflies repels predators. Rainbows visit our valleys in their layered, superb sameness with colors that seem to live and move, while stones hold their brilliant hues in what appears an unshakable permanence. Yet, as dusk daily closes down on the world, all colors—from stone to rainbow—seem to vanish to a black-and-white sleep. Where does color come from? When a flower wilts, where does its color go?

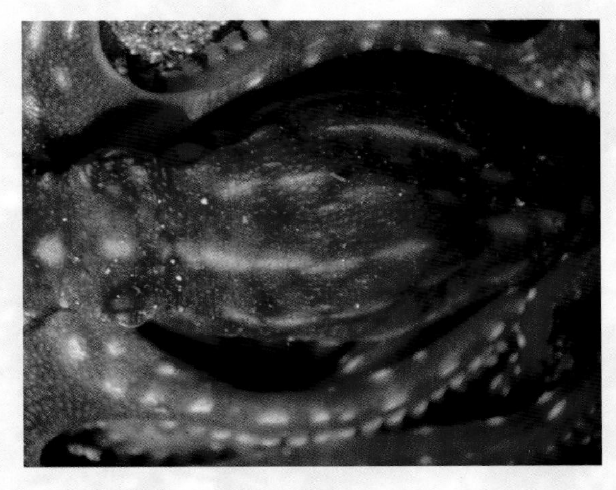

The largest lizard living in Hawai'i is the illegally released green iguana, originally from Central and South America. Frequent sightings in Waimānalo, O'ahu, and the recent discovery there of a clutch of fertilized eggs are proof enough that iguanas are reproducing in the wild. Tongue to tail, these lizards measure up to six feet, two-thirds of which is the thick, muscular tail that can be used like a whip to lash out in defense or as a thrashing motor thrusting the iguana through water. The green iguana is a tree-climber. It can

Iguana

leap from branch to branch and drop fifty feet to the ground unfazed and damage-free. Creased face and fierce gaze mask a mild animal quite content with the quiet privacy of the woods, feeding mostly on a vegetarian diet of leaves, flowers and fruit. In their homeland, iguanas are much esteemed by humans for their light, white meat.

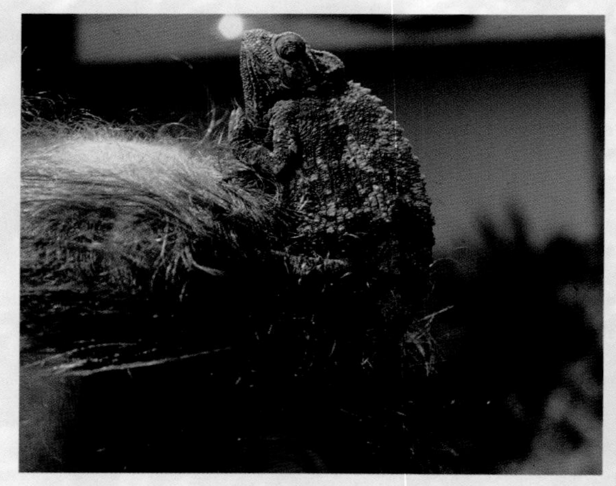

Jackson's chameleon

The two-foot-long Jackson's chameleon is another pet release that has become quite common in the forests of Oʻahu and a serious competitor with native birds for insects and flowers in the high trees. It is truly a fascinating creature, with its three-horned (only in the male), dinosaurlike body, and eyes that swivel independently atop bulgy knobs and are able to track two different insects simultaneously. This chameleon clings to branches with its pincerlike grip and handy wraparound tail that serves as a fifth foot.

Not so sweet-tempered is the occasional alligator or caiman (a crocodile-like relative from Central and South America) that makes its way to island streams or reservoirs. Some years ago a dead alligator got dumped off a bridge into Maunawili Stream on windward Oʻahu; a caiman was killed at the reservoir in upper Nuʻuanu. These were most likely small smuggled-in *moʻo* that soon outgrew their owner's bathtubs or ability to satisfy their growing reptilian appetites. One pet alligator lived for many years on the campus of Saint Louis High School and became quite a public attraction. A teacher named Brother Mathias had brought in the gecko-sized baby alligator in a cigar box from Louisiana. Seventeen years and seven feet later, the alligator died. The year was 1903 and the alligator's death was big news in small-town Honolulu.

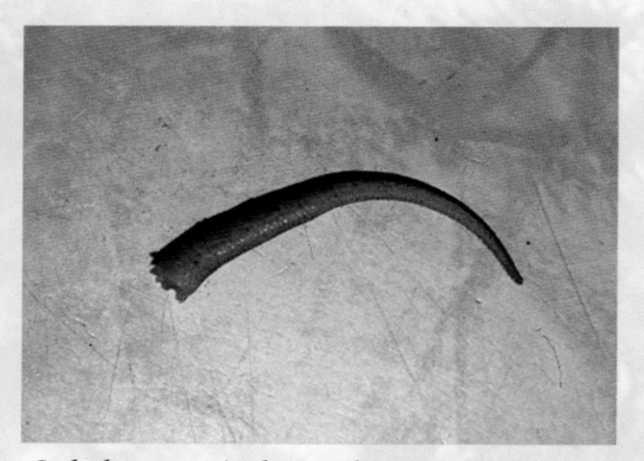

Gecko long gone, its decoy tail remains behind.

Stomping and Chomping

The Pig

Lore and Legend

In Hawaiian culture, pigs were important as food, as payment of rent to chiefs and in religious and ceremonial activities. The darkest of all, the little *hiwahiwa* (precious) pigs, were placed forth on altars to appease and praise the gods, particularly the great god Lono.

Young pigs ran free around family compounds, stayed close to humans and seldom strayed to inland forests, thus having little impact on the fragile island world that had evolved without hoofed, grazing mammals.

Chiefs of old were seen as godly beings residing on Earth. The perceptive, keenly intelligent pig was at times used to search out an *ali'i* in hiding or to locate a burial site of chiefly bones. In one story, the young 'Umi, son of chief Līloa of Waipi'o Valley on the island of Hawai'i, decided to visit his father's lands for the first time. He stopped to make an offering of fish at Laupāhoehoe, a coastal settlement not far from Waipi'o. When a lasting rainbow colored the cliff above his residence there, suspicions stirred as to his identity. The *kahuna* (priest) Ka'olekū was called to the house with a "chief-seeking pig" in arm. After a brief prayer offering, the pig was set down. It strode straight to 'Umi, stopped, stood a moment before the disguised chief, and then raised its snout and folded its front legs under in recognition of an *ali'i*. 'Umi readily admitted to his chiefly bloodline.

Preparing the imu *was men's work in old Hawai'i.*

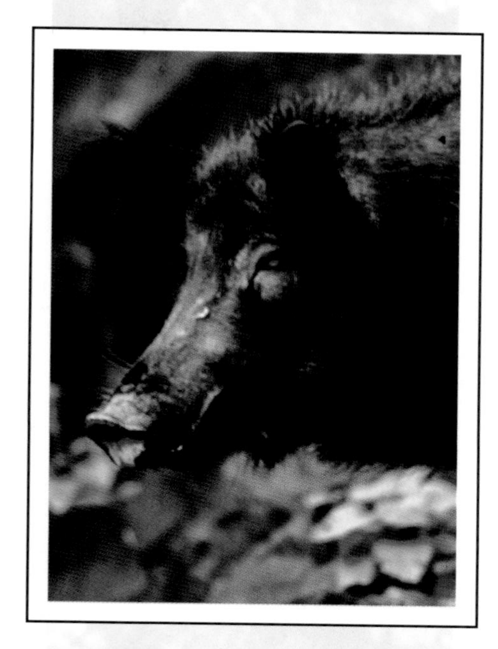

Hawaiian Name: *Pua'a*
Scientific Name: *Sus scrofa*
Area of Origin: Southeast Asia
Date of Arrival: Probable Polynesian import

Pigs were used in traditional rituals, especially as offerings to the gods. The launching of a new canoe, for example, was accompanied by careful preparation to honor Kāne, protector of those who labored at sea. The *imu* (underground oven) was opened with intense suspense: if the pig's skin was glossy and unwrinkled, the canoe would glide smooth and last long. If the skin was cracked and warped, the canoe would soon suffer misfortune.

Older pigs were penned for fattening and tossed scraps of sweet potato, *kalo*, banana and breadfruit. Men steamed pig *kālua* style in the *imu* and then served it in their eating houses, where sacred images were kept and where women and children were not allowed. Only when boys aged six or seven completed rites of passage into manhood were they welcome to eat with their male elders, and pig became part of their diet. A ceremony called Kā i Mua "pushed" the boy out of the women's house for the first time and into the world of men.

In ancient times, a pig grunting in the murky dark was a sign a ghost was near. If you carried cooked pork, hungry ghosts were sure to come at you. Ti leaves tied around the food brought protection.

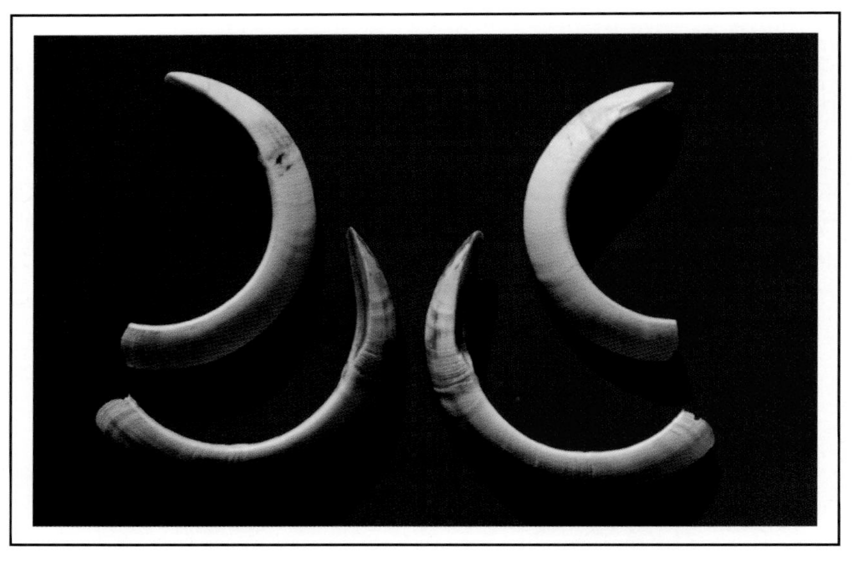

Boar tusks easily chisel up Hawaiian topsoil.

Habitat

It is the "mountain pig," which today roams the high, isolated stretches encircling Mauna Kea and Mauna Loa on the island of Hawai'i, that is thought to resemble most closely the original Polynesian pigs. Mauna Kea mornings dawn cloudless and clear, with a cold that quivers pale. The haze of the day's heat grows gradually till afternoon, when a billow of silent, puffy fog tumbles down the pasture grass into the scattered *māmane* forests. Late afternoon darkness draws the dark pigs from their day hideaways to graze the grass in scattered groups of sows, piglets and young boars mixed among ranch livestock. Living isolated in the remote volcanic highlands, these pigs probably still look a lot like their Polynesian ancestors: small, lean swine with long, slim snouts, short, erect ears and sloping rumps. Thin legs give them a dainty, tippy-toe look—a reminder perhaps of their ancient relative the deer—but they are really quite agile. Alert to an approaching horse or Jeep, they swerve off abruptly in a lock-legged trot of surprising stiff quickness, grunting and snorting, their long, tuft-tipped tails whipping behind them.

The forest pig makes its home in a much more fragile habitat than that of its mountain cousins and has different foraging habits. Captain Cook landed a European-bred sow and boar on Niʻihau on February 2, 1778, together with goats, geese and a variety of vegetable seeds. These and other big domestic pigs, called "Captain Cookers" in the South Pacific, bred with the smaller native pigs. Their hefty offspring drifted away from housesites, becoming feral and eventually populating all the major Hawaiian islands. It is their look-alike descendants that make up the feral pig populations today. Blotchy bristle colorations of white to beige to brown reveal traces of their non-Polynesian past; their boxy appearance and stocky fatness show both their domestic ancestry and their rich forest feedings on fruit, avocado, *kukui* (candlenut) nuts, starchy tree ferns, and worms.

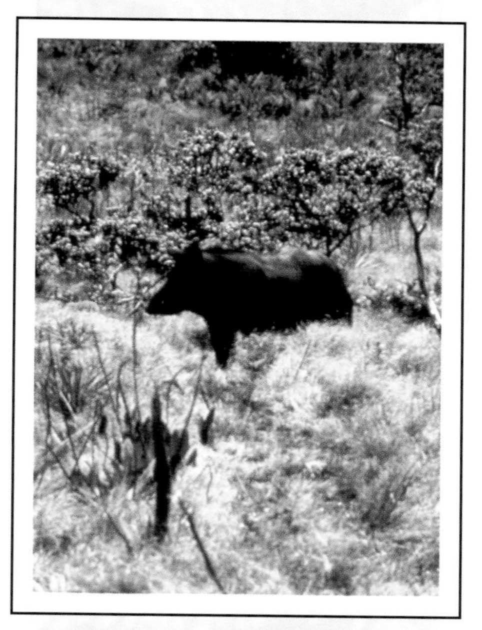

Mountain pig in its habitat

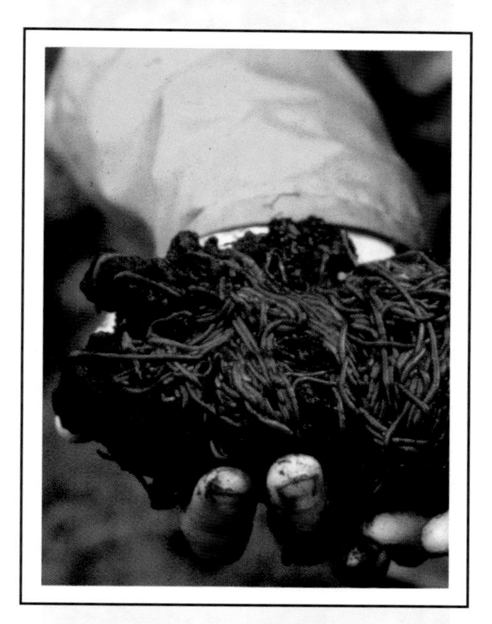

Worms, a pig's delight

Our Hawaiian rain forests are among the most imperiled anywhere; above all else, it is the damage caused by forest pigs along with the invasion of aggressive alien plants that are bringing the devastation. Native Hawaiian species evolved their specialized forms long before humans or any hoofed animals arrived in the islands. Endemic plants are generally thornless, scentless and nonpoisonous, making them defenseless against introduced browsers. Root systems run shallow through the thin layer of forest topsoil and are easily scuffed up by hooves or snuffed up by keen-scenting snouts. While accessible areas are effectively protected by routine hunting, extremely rugged and remote regions of fragile native vegetation—such as the cloud forests near the summits—are hard to get at for hunters and their dogs. Pigs crisscross this rough terrain with swift ease, passing into pristine areas where they open wide wounds with their rootings.

The Nature Conservancy and other groups have attempted to reduce pig populations through snaring, fencing, and trapping, but have met the angry opposition of many local hunters, who feel deprived of good sport, good food, and what they resolutely see as their cultural right. Hunters and environmentalists have frequently gone nose-to-nose over these issues. The ideal solution might allow for hunting zones where traditional hunting rights would be respected, at the same time that increased protection of the most threatened areas is guaranteed.

Views

"Since feral pigs has been here over 100 years or more why not take advantage of their existence? Open up more areas to accommodate the hunting community for recreational hunting, subsistence and for training of future generations. Cooperation by state, U.S. Government and private land owners with the hunting community to properly control the feral pig population in their habitat is a win-win situation."

(Pascual Dabis, President, O'ahu Pig Hunters Association, personal communication to author, 1999)

"[A] lot of people here think of pigs as native animals. They don't understand why we are trying to control them. The school system lets us down badly. The local schools don't teach Hawaiian natural history. We have a huge education effort at hand. We've got to manage the resource and educate people as to why. There's a lot of misunderstanding on why we manage the park the way we do. We're tolerated by most people, understood by a few, disliked by some. Recreational pig hunters—the Hawaiians who hunt for meat—are the most hostile."

(Dan Taylor, U.S. Park Service Ranger, from "The Pig War" by Kenneth Brower, in Stewart, 1992.)

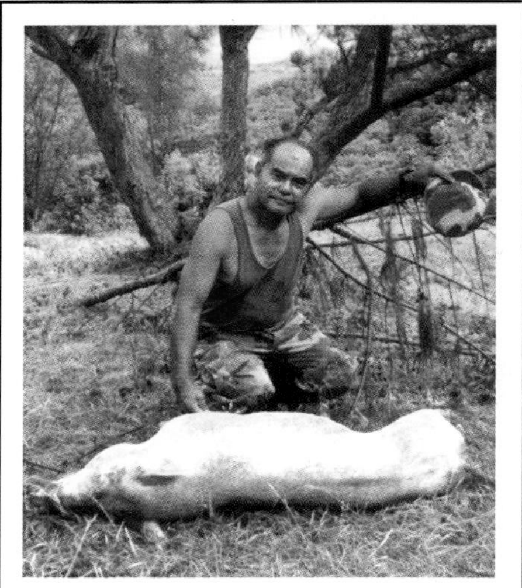

Hunter Pascual Dabis and a "Captain Cooker"

Food

Pigs of old grazed grass, rooted insects and worms, and fed on the forest plants, among them the mountain apple, ti leaf, *kukui* and starchy tree fern. Today, of the many tasty fruits in the Hawaiian rain forest that pigs relish, the most environmentally nasty are the introduced guava, strawberry guava and banana poka. Pigs follow the fruiting seasons of these plants, feed heavily, then move away into other areas, where they sleep or graze, hauling a bellyful of digesting fruit with them. The stony seeds pass through the pigs and are deposited on the ground with a rich dose of fertilizing manure, thus spreading the exotic plants further across the Hawaiian landscape. Guavas grow in a bullying tangle of trees, while the banana poka rises in a webwork of suffocating vine high onto the forest canopy, stealing the sunshine that normally sifts downward to the ferny floor. Forest pigs have learned to grab the trailing vines of banana poka and thrash them sideways to make ripe fruit fall.

Just Wondering

Little wonder perhaps that pigs spend so much time focused on food. Taste and smell are keenly refined senses in these animals, more highly developed than in humans. Compare these facts: the tissue in the back of a human nose that is used to identify smells measures about two square inches. In a pig, the same tissue covers as much as twenty-five square inches. Can we imagine what a rich experience such a snout must provide? As for taste buds, pigs also come in far ahead of humans, some fifteen thousand buds to about ten thousand in humans. Many other animals have similarly developed senses that far outperform those of humans. Are we slow to realize how different and remarkable the senses of other creatures might be?

Piglets; striped patterning disappears as they grow older.

Reproduction

Wild sows can produce two litters a year averaging five to six piglets each. Boars tend to be solitary, except in mating season, when they meet up with sows. After mating, the female carries her young four months and then carefully prepares a birthing nest. She gathers dry grasses and ferns to a pile in a sheltered place at the lee of a tree trunk, a heap of rocks or bushes, where she lies as she births and nurses her piglets.

A piglet slips from its mother sleek, wriggly and wet, with eyes sealed, its pointed snout nuzzling out a nearby nipple. Each piglet finds a nipple and then returns to the same nipple as long as it sucks. With the richest milk supply located near the sow's head, the piglets up front get the best milk. For the first weeks, nursing is the only source of food for the piglets, and the protein-rich milk makes for quick growth. At twenty or so days, the piglets are trotting alongside the sow, talkative and inquisitive, copying her grazing and grunting and rooting, crouching motionless at the slightest warning snort. They continue to nurse for three to four months, at which time the sow drives them off or simply leaves them.

Just Wondering

Mother pig, like many other animals, is so devoted to her offspring that she will unhesitatingly risk her life defending them. For a time, that is. When they reach a certain age, it seems she just as eagerly drives them away or abandons them. What has changed?

More Pig Facts

In days past, when special visitors arrived, a pig was cooked for a welcoming feast. If a person committed a wrong against a neighbor, a hog was killed and offered with prayers of forgiveness to the offended one. The offering could not be refused. Custom required that the two people make up, feast together on the new-baked pig, make merry and then sleep under the same roof.

Young Hawaiians in ancient times celebrated the hard learning that went into acquiring a profession or skill—but not by dressing up in cap and gown and proudly walking across a stage to receive a diploma. Graduation in those days was a ceremony called ʻAilolo, "Eating the Brains." Pig brains were offered in reverence and gratitude to the god who watched over a particular art or craft; the youth would then eat of the sacred offering as a powerful symbol of his or her passage into the area of expertise.

Weighing in at three, four and sometimes five hundred pounds, the hugely powerful forest pigs have a more severe impact on their habitat than their mountain cousins. Their tough snouts and chisel-like tusks can churn up a sizable chunk of the fragile Hawaiian rain forest in a few brief hours before dawn, thrusting aside boulders, tractoring up roots, crushing tree ferns in an area the size of a standard living-room floor. As they plow up these areas, they also fertilize them with their droppings. Pigs introduce alien species on their bristles and in their excrement. Exotic grasses—adapted as they are to rich soils and fertile seedbeds—gain a foothold in disturbed areas. With up to 300 pigs per square mile roaming Hawaiʻi's forests, the total nightly damage can be significant:

Views

"The [Europeans] brought in their nasty guys and they mixed with the tamer Hawaiian pigs, and at some point they started getting loose and went nuts. Now they're loose in the forest causing havoc. They're like 300-pound organic Rototillers, putting big holes in the ground which lets exotic plants fill the gap. Or they create muddy water puddles where mosquitoes breed and transfer diseases such as avian malaria to the native bird population. . . . The pigs are the top of the food chain. We don't have any wild predator that preys on pigs. So man is an essential ingredient."

(Curt Cottrell, Program Manager, Nā Ala Hele Trail Management Program, State of Hawaiʻi, Honolulu Advertiser, *September. 8, 1998)*

Gleaming tusks break the gum line on either side of a young boar's bottom jaw. As the boar grows, the deeply rooted tusk curves up and round and sharp like a new moon. An upper canine tooth grows down and slightly forward; when the boar's mouth is closed, the top tooth fits flush against the rising tusk. Constant grinding against the upper tooth hones the tusk's edge to a knife-blade sharpness. When boars get agitated or angry, they excitedly grate and grind their tusks to razor readiness, whetting them as they go, wetting them with a drippy wipe of drool. These tusks are feeding-tools that tear and rip and shred. Powered by thick chests and muscled, cartilage-padded shoulders that provide a natural "shield," the tusks are also formidable weapons that slash and gash a foe: they command great respect. In days past, a warrior brave in battle was referred to as "a fierce-rooting hog."

In old Hawai'i and throughout the South Pacific, tusks were prized possessions. In Vanuatu, for example, the number and value of boars' tusks that a man could accumulate determined his status in the community. The upper canine teeth of young boars were cracked off. With nothing to grind against, the lower tooth kept growing and curving back until it dug into the pig's cheek, then down through his jaw, completing the circle. This took about seven years and resulted in circular tusks of great value. More rare and precious yet were tusks that went on to curl a second circle.

Mud-splattered dogs snap and grab at a cornered pig.

A long-popular way of hunting wild pigs in the islands is by using dogs to chase down, then hold down the pig. The grabber dog gets the pig by the snout or ear and holds it tight to the ground while the hunter grips a hind leg or the tail, flips the pig over, then slips his knife deep into its heart or slits its throat. The role of the dog is crucial and precarious: many are cut up and killed by furious boars. Even without the boar's razor tusks, the sow's angry jaws can crush a human wrist like a pretzel. More than one hunter has been killed and many maimed terribly by pigs that have wrung themselves free:

Views

"I recall selling a hunting license to a man who had to use both hands to hold his pen as he signed his name; both arms were bandaged to the elbow. I asked him what the trouble was and he casually stated that his dogs had let go of a boar just as he grabbed for it; the boar's tusks had severed all the tendons on both wrists, but he was undaunted and intended to go hunting again as soon 'as I can close my fingers to hold a knife!' "

(R.J. Kramer, 1971)

Field biologists do not know if wild pigs in Hawai'i sniff beaches to snout out turtle eggs. Elsewhere, in places such as the Galápagos Islands, egg destruction by hungry beachcombing pigs is a serious problem.

A pig passed here.

WESTERN SETTLEMENT: MANY NEW THINGS

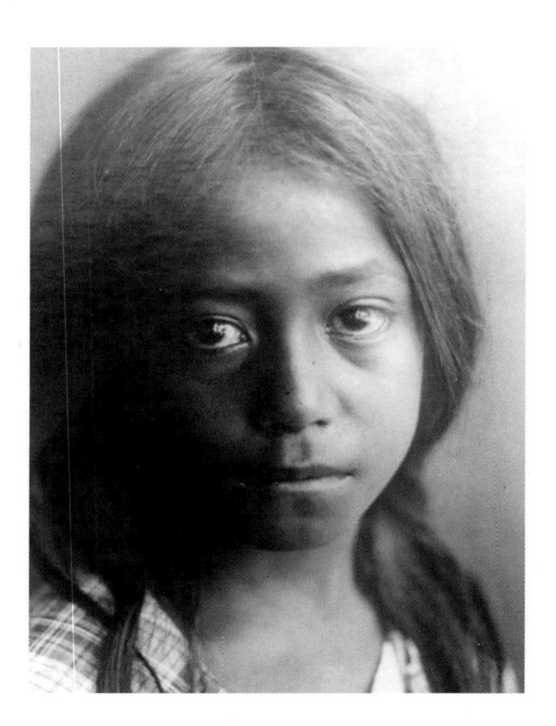

Views

"Now come new kinds of axes from the lands of the white man. . . . The stone-ax is laid aside. . . . New species of birds have been introduced, also new kinds of cloth, so that the former kapa *cloth has almost entirely gone out of use. There are also new tools, books, and laws, many new things. . . . These things are late importations; the number of such things will doubtless increase in the future."*

(D. Malo, trans. N.B. Emerson, 1898)

"Only with the appearance of the white man another era dawned; he at once bound this isolated group to the five continents, and established a highway on which what lived or breathed in distant regions might wend its way hither."

(W. Hillebrand, 1856, in Kay, 1972)

"God said unto man, be fruitful and multiply, and replenish the Earth and subdue it, and have dominion over the fish of the sea and over the fowl of the air and over every living thing that moveth upon the Earth."

(Book of Genesis, Old Testament)

On the morning of January 18, 1778, Captain James Cook first set sight on the Hawaiian Islands. Cook's small, crowded ships, the *Discovery* and the *Resolution*, were typical of most exploration vessels of his day. They were in part floating farms, carrying goats, cats, geese, ducks and other animals, none of which had previously been seen in Hawai'i. Many ships had kitchen gardens as well, small planter boxes on deck where manure from shipboard animals was mixed with a bit of ballast soil to provide seedbed.

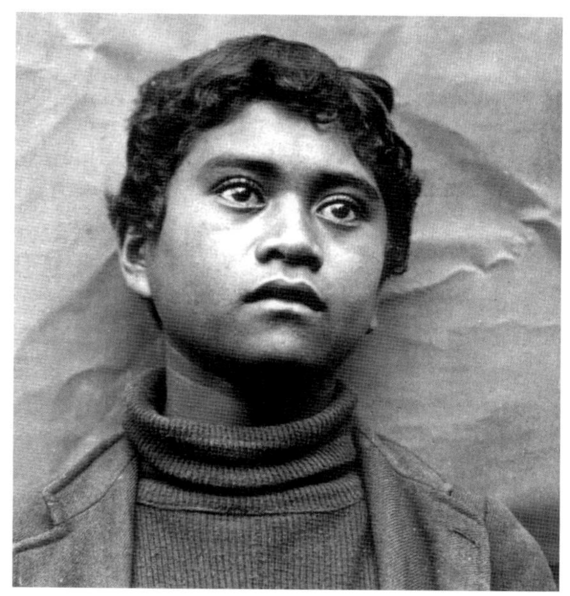

Transported Landscapes: The Land Forever Changed

Captain Cook landed animals and set seeds wherever he went throughout the Pacific, sometimes as gifts to native chiefs, but also to provision ports of call for his own return visits. Goats were commonly released on outlying islands to provide food for castaways. In Hawai'i, Cook first made landfall on Ni'ihau, where, "being very desirous of benefiting these poor people, by furnishing them with some additional articles of food," he left pumpkin, melon and onion seeds as well as sheep, goats and large European pigs.

Some scientists use the term "transported landscapes" to describe how a voyaging people will take a whole new set of plants and animals to their destination, completely transforming the original landscape with their own introductions. Arriving *haole* ships, like the Polynesian voyaging canoes that had come before them, did indeed carry a new world of plants and animals to these fragile islands, forever changing the former landscape.

A Race Decreases: With Death Every Day

The most dreadful introductions in those first days of foreign contact were the many contagious diseases hiding in a deathly silence within the bodies of sailors. Like the endemic species of the native forest—the thornless raspberry, the scentless mint, the flightless bird—Hawaiians were defenseless against bacteria and viruses their ancestors' bodies had never known. The deaths to come were horrific. These figures point to a pain that our experience cannot comprehend.

Year	Estimated Native Hawaiian Population
1778	400,000–1 million
1802	200,000
1853	72,000
1887	40,000

A deadly epidemic, thought to have been cholera, struck O'ahu in 1804, just as Kamehameha the Great and his warriors were preparing to invade Kaua'i. Thousands

died as their body fluids drained away in what Hawaiians called "the squatting disease." Here is an account from 1863 by a witness to this terrible time:

Views

"Dear Newspaper Kū'oko'a:
I am one who asked a certain old man of the time of Kamehameha I about the epidemic disease called 'the squatting sickness' and he told me. Below is what he related to me.
The squatting disease was one in which numerous men, women, and children died and it was this sickness that killed the majority of the people. There was no other disease like it.
Most of the people in different places throughout the islands died within one day—40 in certain places, 80 in certain places, 120 in other places and 400 in other places . . . it was in areas where many people lived that most of the deaths occurred.
The length of the ravages of this disease on the people of these islands was three or perhaps more months, with deaths every day. This is the reason for the great decrease in this race."

(W. Kahala, Nūpepa Kū'oko'a, *February, 1863, trans. author)*

Similar accounts appeared with horrid frequency in Hawaiian language newspapers throughout the second half of the nineteenth century. The following is a description of the deadly smallpox epidemic that struck Maui in the 1850s, leaving thousands dead:

Views

"The dead fell like dried kukui *twigs tossed down by the wind. Day by day from morning till night horse-drawn carts went about from street to street of the town, and the dead were stacked up like a load of wood, some in coffins, but most of them just piled in, wrapped in cloth with heads and legs sticking out. . . . The whole population was wiped out from Waikū, the uplands of Kawaipapa, Palemo and* ma uka *of Waika'akihi in the Hāna district, and so for Kipahulu and Kaupō. . . . For six months the epidemic lasted, by October its rage seemed spent. Ten thousand of the people are said to have died of this disease."*

(S. Kamakau, trans. M.K. Pukui, 1976)

Bellies of shipboard stock carried their inner cargo of flukes, tapeworms and flatworms, and fleas and flies bred in their fur. In the bowels of the ships themselves, heaps of ballast soil, pitched in as a stabilizing weight, teemed with foreign insects. When these piles of soil and rock were shoveled onshore to make room for outgoing cargo, scorpions, centipedes, earthworms and scores of other creatures crawled quietly into Hawai'i. Shipboard vegetable bins were regularly flung open and aired out near shore, releasing little clouds of newly hatched insects to drift inland. Hawser ropes mooring ships to land provided perfect passage to shore for debarking rats and roaches. The tree-climbing roof rat probably stole off such a docked ship and slipped high into native forests to join the Polynesian rat in feeding on birds and tree snails.

From Isolation to "Crossroads of the Pacific"

The harboring in Hawai'i of foreign fleets was at full force by the mid-1800s: the ports of Lahaina and Honolulu were so thick with the masts of ships that Hawaiians referred to these places as floating forests. On a single day in 1852, 149 ships could be counted moored in the port of Honolulu. The isolation that had at once created and protected these unique islands was forever lost. Winds that for millions of years had brought the occasional colonizer and a life-giving rain to this hidden world now were called "trade winds" and whisked flotillas of trading ships to and from this valuable "Crossroads of the Pacific," a place that was assuming great commercial importance.

The Undoing of a World: From All Sides Unabatingly

Livestock, released by the early visiting ships and protected with a *kapu* against their killing by Hawaiian *ali'i*, had reproduced to huge herds and were now browsing out native habitats, bruising the land and forcing endemic birds and tree snails farther into back forests. One observer noted the destruction by cattle as "the greatest evil from which we are now suffering as a people . . . sometimes [cattle] would eat the very thatch off the sides of the native huts." Sheep and goats were devastating their own habitats of choice, while shipboard cats, now gone feral, were preying heavily on forest birds.

The attack on this ancient and unique island world came from all sides, unabatingly.

A "floating forest" of foreign masts, Honolulu Harbor, 1850s

Views

"Forest fires, animals and agriculture have so changed the islands, within the last fifty or sixty years, that one can now travel for miles, in some districts, without finding a single indigenous plant; the ground being wholly taken possession of by weeds, shrubs, and grasses, imported from various countries. It is remarkable that plants from both tropical and temperate regions seem to thrive equally well on these islands, many of them spreading as if by magic, and rapidly exterminating much of the native flora."

(I. Sinclair, 1885, quoted in Kay, 1972)

"The disturbance caused by the entrance of cattle into untrodden forest appears to be alone sufficient to scare away some species. Thus, on a very rough lava flow on Hawai'i in 1892, the 'ō'ō (Acrulocercus nobilis) *was very numerous, and as many as a dozen of these birds could be seen in a single tree, making, with hosts of the scarlet* 'i'iwi, *the crimson* 'apapane, *and other birds, a picture never to be forgotten. A few years afterwards, on revisiting the spot at the same season, although the trees were, as before, one mass of flowers, hardly a single* 'ō'ō *was to be seen. The only noticeable change was that cattle were wandering over the flow and beginning to destroy the brushwood, just as they had already reduced the formerly dense forest bordering the flow to the condition of open park-land. . . . We have known a forest so dense that it could be traversed only along a narrow made path, generally knee-deep in mud, to be reduced to open woodland by the ravages of cattle within a period of about fifteen years."*

(R.C.L. Perkins, 1913)

As farming grew in the islands, enterprising growers brought in a variety of quality breeding animals to improve and expand their stock. The silkworm and honeybee were introduced as well in the hope of providing cash crops. From 1850

Steers bound for slaughterhouse

Arriving Chinese immigrants, Honolulu Harbor, 1860s

to 1880, some twenty different game birds were shipped in by eager sportsmen. Rabbits were released on several of the small coastal islands, which provided perfect natural "hutches" for huge populations of easily shot game, as described in this turn-of-the-century article:

Views

"The reason for naming it Rabbit Island [off Waimānalo, Oʻahu, still called Mānana by many Hawaiians] is made quickly apparent to the visitor who approaches it in a boat. Almost every foot of the ground is seen to be occupied by a rabbit; in fact it is one of the most thickly populated rabbit colonies in the world. A few of the small rodents were taken there many years ago by some party or parties unknown. . . . They have so denuded the place of all edible vegetation that they are obliged to subsist on small shell fish which they find along the beach. There being no spring there, they get drinking water from dew and rain deposits."

(Paradise of the Pacific, *August, 1901)*

By the mid-1800s, much of the lowland had been wiped clean of native species. To fill the void, newspapers periodically ran articles urging people embarking on foreign trips to bring back whatever seeds, plants and birds they could to provide food, shade and pretty songs to local residents.

Just Wondering

What a mishmash of species humans have hurriedly cluttered together on these lovely little islands! After millions of years of steady, tidy crafting, what is evolution to make of it all?

Among the early settlers to Hawaiʻi were several ethnic groups drawn to the islands by the opportunity of field labor in

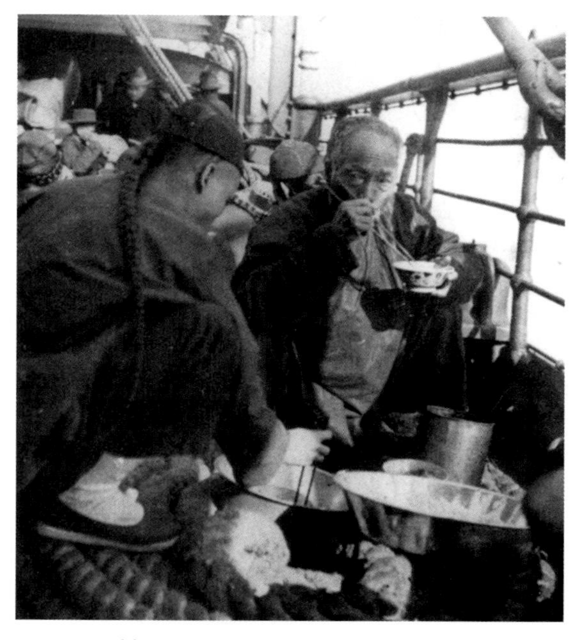

Room and board for Chinese immigrants, circa 1865

The hard labor of the cane field shows on these immigrant faces.

the growing sugar industry. In 1848, the Great Māhele moved the control of land away from the Hawaiian chiefs and into private ownership. Many non-Hawaiians bought up vast areas and began the cultivation of sugar, coffee, rice, silk, and other crops. So many Hawaiians had died from the ravaging diseases that the new landowners turned abroad for field-workers. Each immigrant group brought with it from the homeland plants and animals that were tasty or pretty or just useful to have in a new land. Added to these were the hundreds of species that silently, invisibly were making their way to these islands: it has been estimated that over eight thousand kinds of exotic plants and animals have come to Hawai'i over these years. The land was changing greatly, and man's relationship to the land was also changing.

Just Wondering

Do we belong to the land or does the land belong to us?

By 1900, the cutting of native forest land had so denuded Hawaiian hills that real public concern arose about conditions in the precious watershed areas that provided drinking water to a growing population and irrigation to the huge fields of sugar that now carpeted the *'āina*. Government programs set to the task of reforestation. Unfortunately, rather than selecting native trees that were deemed too slow-growing, officials planted quick-growing alien species such as eucalyptus and Norfolk pine. These species, not having evolved in Hawai'i, are unsuitable host plants for endemic species.

Views

"[M]ore than 10,000 plants were distributed in May and June to the general public, with nearly 13,000 to plantation and other companies, by the government nursery. On top of these numbers the nurseryman engaged to deliver 50,000 seedlings between the middle of July and the end of August to such operations. Here is a faint idea of what is doing in forestation in these islands."

(Paradise of the Pacific, *September, 1915*)

"Bulbs from Holland, orchids from New Jersey and Australia, wax palms from Singapore, chrysanthemums and peach blossoms from Japan, and ginseng roots from Korea were among the recent interesting importations."

(Paradise of the Pacific, *April, 1916*)

Just Wondering

Some four thousand plant species from other lands, other climates made their way to Hawai'i. In bringing their blooming and fruiting cycles from other places, did these plants impose a new sense of seasons on this land that Hawaiians never knew? Are "spring," "summer," "fall," and "winter" exotic intruders of our minds, displacing an older sense of time and place in Hawai'i—in the same way that these plants have completely replaced the original native biota?

Cane train, Waimānalo, O'ahu, date unknown

Introduced to control rats, the day-feeding mongoose more often preyed on ground-nesting birds.

Red-footed booby chick, injured by mongoose, Ulupa'u Crater, O'ahu

When cash crops such as sugarcane and rice replaced subsistence farming, pests increased in the single-crop plantations. Many new species of birds and insects were imported and released to fight the agricultural pests. This pattern of bringing in new species to solve problems created by previously introduced plants or animals is a common theme in Hawai'i's natural history. The blackberry, for example, was brought in to provide field feed for the many game birds that arrived after the mid-1800s. It has since become a serious habitat nuisance. The mongoose, intentionally released at Hāmākua, Hawai'i, in 1883 to kill introduced rats, encountered few rodents during its daytime prowlings. Instead, it became a deadly predator of ground-nesting birds, joining the feral cat, by now an oldtimer in the islands:

Views

"Cats were introduced into the Hawaiian Islands at a very early time, and, no doubt, increased excessively, while, as their owners moved from place to place, many strayed into the woods and began to feed on mice, rats, and birds. They are now found wild on all the islands, apparently only the wettest portions of the forest being free from them. On Lāna'i, in walking up a single ravine, I counted the remains of no less than twenty-two native birds killed by cats, and these must all have been destroyed within two days as previously the whole gulch had been washed out by a heavy flood. Two cats were actually shot on this occasion as they were devouring their prey, and several others seen, but, owing to the fact that they are extremely shy and mostly nocturnal in habits, few people who have not lived much in the woods have any idea of their numbers. The common rat is also quite at home in the forests and is decidedly arboreal in habits, feeding on fruits, land mollusks, and no doubt on birds. The mynah, which I have myself seen devouring both young and eggs of other species, has increased prodigiously, and probably exceeds in numbers the whole of the native land birds put together. It has greatly extended its range through the forest since 1892, and on some of the islands it is now ubiquitous."

(R.C.L. Perkins, 1913)

The end of living: Once "laid out with great neatness," these taro fields today lie abandoned, mute and clogged with alien vegetation.

The slow creation of the Hawaiian world happened over tens of millions of years, one plant, one animal at a time. The undoing of that world is happening at a pace that is horrifically quick, one plant, one animal at a time.

Just Wondering

Hawaiians were among many indigenous peoples whose relationship to the land has changed dramatically. The pain, fear and questioning that came with such change are poignantly expressed for all by Chief Joseph, leader of the Nez Percé tribe of eastern Oregon and Washington State:

"How can you buy or sell the sky, the warmth of the land? The idea is strange to us. If we do not own the freshness of the air and the sparkle of the water, how can you buy them?"

(Adapted from a speech by Chief Joseph, 1854)

"The whites too shall pass—perhaps sooner than other tribes. Continue to contaminate your bed and you will one night suffocate in your own waste. When the buffalo are all slaughtered, the horses all tamed, the secret corners of the forest heavy with the scent of many men, and the view of the hills blotted by talking wires, where then is the thicket? Gone. Where is the eagle? Gone. And what is to say good-bye to the swift and the hunt, the end of living and the beginning of survival?

(Adapted from a speech by Chief Joseph, 1855)

Hawaiian Name: *'Elelū*
Area of Origin:
Africa and Central Asia
Date of Arrival: Late 1700s (?)

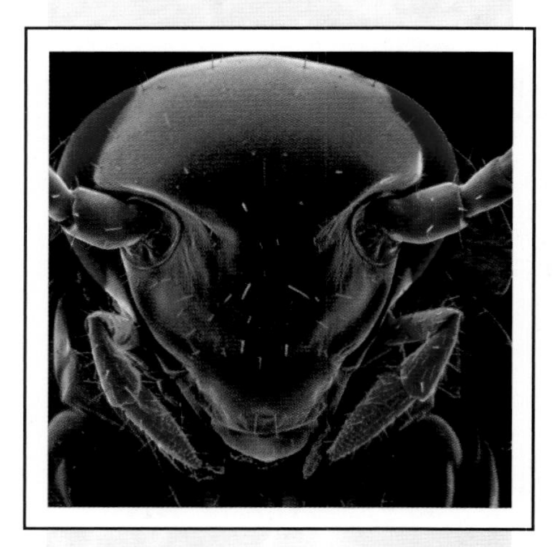

Head-on view of a German cockroach, magnified 17 times

Ever and Forever Pest

The Cockroach

Arrival in Hawai'i

The first cockroaches may have joined the gecko and rat as stowaways onboard early Polynesian voyaging canoes. More likely, however, they jumped ship off one of the many foreign vessels that set anchor here in the late 1700s, all of which were infested with several types of roaches. One account relates that the roach problem onboard was generally so bad that sailors took to wearing mittens at night to keep their fingernails from being gnawed to the quick.

Within a few years, Honolulu and other towns were teeming with roaches, as related by this early report:

Views

"At night, multitudes of cockroaches descended from their daytime quarters in thatched roofs and elsewhere and attacked in swarms, crawling over noses and eyelids of would-be sleepers. If a handkerchief was put on the face, they snaked beneath it; if one turned over and lay face down, they scampered along unhindered."

(Captain Jacobus Boelen, visiting Honolulu in 1828)

Habitat

At present, there are at least nineteen species of cockroaches in Hawai'i, living in many different types of habitats. Some occupy the same warm, humid living conditions as humans and for that reason have long been common household pests, slipping their flat bodies into kitchen cracks by day and darting about after dark. The roach's scientific family name, *Blatta,* refers to a creature that shuns the light, an appropriate word for this brusque, six-legged critter that scurries away when the kitchen light suddenly flashes on.

Views

"The cockroach is probably the most obnoxious insect known to man."

(P. B. Cornwell, 1968)

Food

Insects such as the caterpillar, cockroach and termite that feed by chewing up leaves, wood and other organic matter move their jaws sideways, not up and down. These insects have a double set of mouth parts, one set sharp and strong that bites and a second set that holds food and moves it into the mouth. Roaches do at times give humans small clamplike nips.

Cockroaches thrive on any organic material—from kitchen crumbs to leather book bindings, waste paper and each other. They are equipped with special sensor hairs that allow food sampling before swallowing. This taste test may help them to avoid poisons set out by exasperated humans. Roaches easily cope by eating soap, glue, paper or just about anything else they can scavenge. Without any food at all a roach can make do three months by drawing on its own body fats. It can also survive a month without water. This makes cockroaches easygoing passengers, and many a roach has traveled to distant shores sealed inside a harmless-looking package.

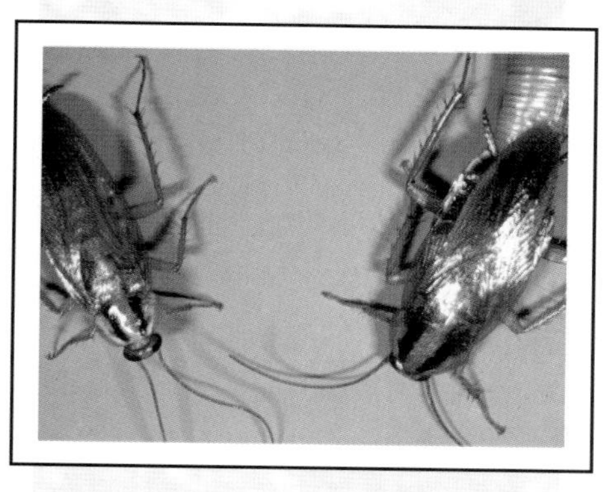

German cockroach; female carries egg case.

Reproduction

The female roach packages her eggs in a bean-shaped, reddish brown case. Beneath the zigzag seam are two rows of tiny chambers, each housing its roach. The female of one species, the smaller but common German cockroach, is frequently seen with the case protruding from her abdomen. She holds on to the case, sheltering the young until they hatch. In other species, the female tears open the egg case when her young are ready to exit.

German cockroach egg case

Generally, roaches in Hawaiʻi paste the case in a safe, concealed place. The satchel swells; its seam splits like a zipper. Pale, soft-skinned young emerge, standing together in a little quivering huddle as their skins harden and darken. Soon they are off, scampering and scrambling, causing endless human consternation.

Growing quickly, young roaches shed their skins as many as twelve times before attaining adult size. The reddish American roach reaches a length of nearly two inches and lives up to four years. During this time the female produces scores of egg capsules.

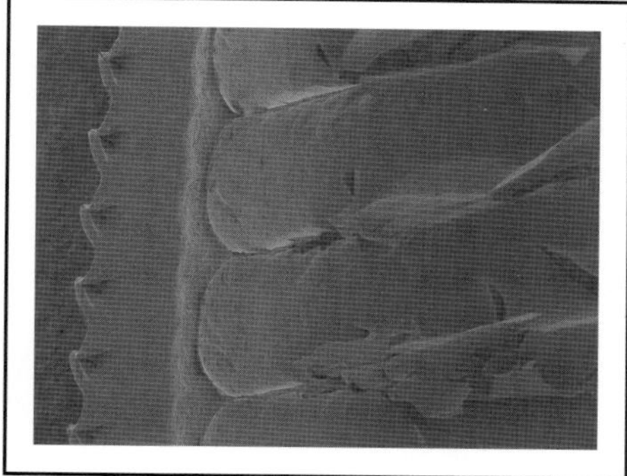

Cockroach egg case, magnified 20 times

Just Wondering

Why do roaches almost always drop dead belly-up?

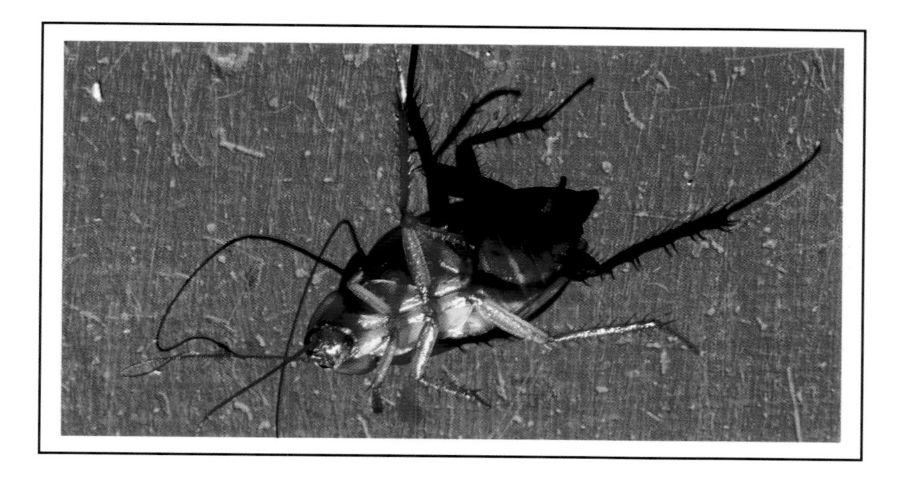

More Cockroach Facts

Fossils show that cockroaches have changed little in appearance in the past 300 million years. Superbly equipped, their creepy-crawly bodies are armored with a shielding, waterproof coating. The waxy coating helps keep their body fluids in and also allows them to swim underwater for short distances without drowning. The thick body wall, called an exoskeleton, shields the roach from high levels of radiation as well as very low temperatures. Hairs protruding through the exoskeleton are keenly pressure sensitive, immediately alerting the roach to a threatening movement. A roach can feel the vibrations of another roach's tiptoe footsteps or those made by a rolled-up newspaper being raised for the swat. The pressure-sensitive hairs bypass the brain by sending warnings directly to the legs by means of impulses that travel along nerve fibers at an amazing fifteen feet per second: the alarm starts them scampering. In short, the roach survives; some humans, weary of the war, predict that this pest will inherit the Earth.

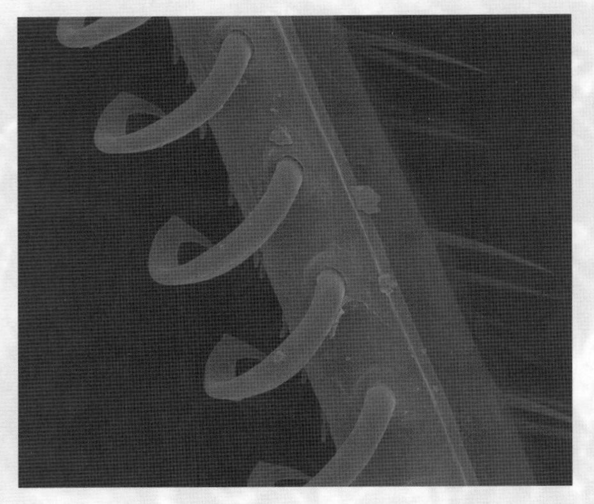

Roach wing edge, magnified 300 times; for improved lift, paired roach wings can lock together.

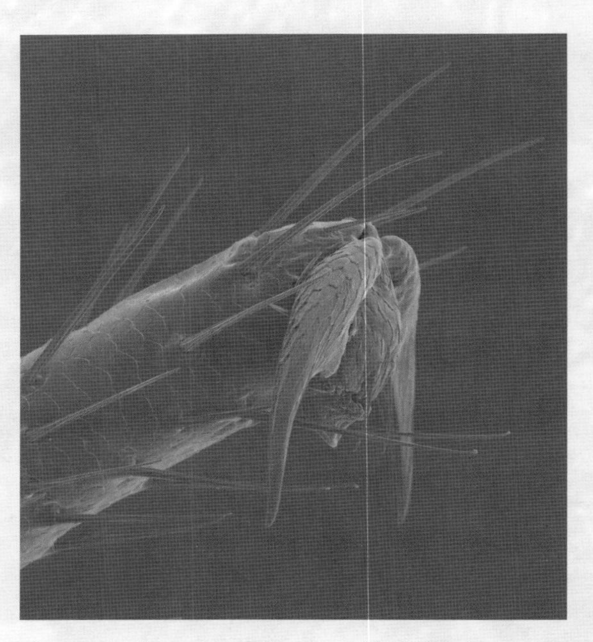

Sensory hairs on roach leg, magnified 350 times

Just Wondering

The roach, like so many of the "lower" animals, has evolved extraordinary technology. The hawk, for example, has incredible sight, up to eight times sharper than that of humans; the dog has a highly acute sense of smell. Geckos scoot across ceilings upside down, and kōlea *fly thousands of miles nonstop. What's more, most mammals can flap their ears. So what makes humans so superior?*

At one time it was believed that cockroaches hatched out of dried crumbs left in untidy kitchens. An Old World bugaboo belief went something like this: to rid a house of roaches, wrap a big dead one in a piece of paper together with a coin, give the little present to another person, and the pests that infest your home will move to his house. These days Americans use another kind of paper to combat roaches: some 500 million dollar bills are spent on insecticides annually.

In many parts of the world cockroaches were formerly used in medicines to cure a variety of illnesses, including cancer, arthritis, indigestion and ulcers. They are now recognized as carriers, not preventers of disease. Many roaches carry their fill of disease-causing viruses and bacteria. It is not known if cockroaches affect native Hawaiian animals and plants as well as humans.

In Hawai'i, at least nineteen different kinds of roaches thrive in our warm, humid climate. Humans have brought in numerous natural enemies to fight them, including the mynah bird and the mongoose, the bufo, cockroach wasp and a number of smaller wasps that prey on roaches' eggs. Results have been mixed. The bufo seems to be one of the more effective introduced predators. An early experiment tracked a female bufo that lived sixteen years and slurped up some 72,000 cockroaches. But roaches bustle about our homes as if nothing has been done. One scientist calculated that for each roach you see in your kitchen, another fifty or so are lurking just out of sight. Someone has wryly suggested that the only lasting solution might be to put up little mirrors all around the house. Catching a glimpse of its ugly face in the mirror will so frighten the roach that it will flee the place forever.

A scientist has found that the average cockroach breaks wind every fifteen seconds.

To this day, roaches roam the world—and beyond—with impunity. In 1984, a stowaway roach was spotted onboard the Apollo XII command module *Yankee Clipper*. For all anyone knows, the roach traveled to the moon and back, or perhaps snuck onto the lunar module and descended to the surface of the moon. Roaches have even infested cyberspace. Check them out at
http://www.kingroach. com/cockroach.html.
Or try
http://www.nj.com/yucky/roaches/index. html.

Just Wondering

Top speed for the big red roach that skitters across our kitchen floors is about fifty-nine inches a second. What's its mph?

Mouth of Death

The Common Night-Biting Mosquito

Hawaiian Name: *Makika*
Scientific Name: *Culex quinquefasciatus*
Area of Origin: Mexico
Date of Arrival: 1826

Arrival in Hawaiʻi

There are several stories about how the mosquito first made its way to Hawaiʻi. One places the blame on a disgruntled ship captain who spitefully released mosquitoes in Honolulu to get even following an argument with several Hawaiians. Another tells of a homesick gentleman from New England who so missed his native Massachusetts in all its varied ways, including the itchy annoyance of summer mosquitoes, that he imported a modest swarm to help him feel at home.

The most likely account, however, is that of a ship named the *Wellington* that sailed from San Blas, Mexico, and set to at Lahaina, Maui, in the year 1826. Sailors lugged barrels offboard and went *ma uka* to replenish the water supply for the onward voyage. The water left in the bottom of some of the barrels probably carried mosquito wrigglers, which washed into Lahaina Stream as the sailors rinsed out the casks. Some days later a *haole* missionary, the Rev. William Richards, stationed in Lahaina Uka, wrote in his diary of the excitement of local *kānaka* (men) in having first seen what they described to him as "singing flies." Several had reddish blotches on their skin, which he recognized as mosquito bites.

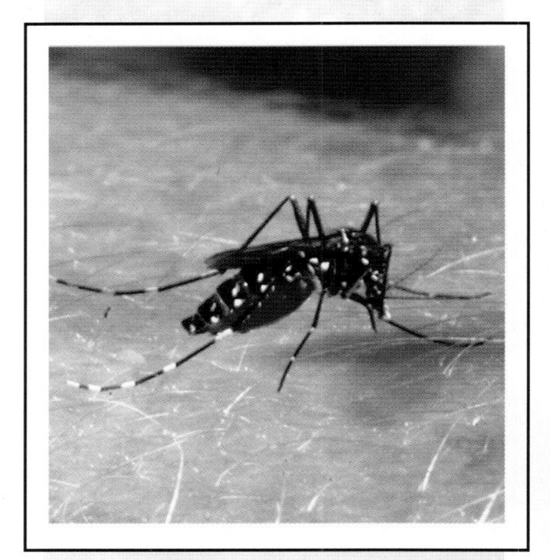

Forest Day mosquito "bites" human hand.

Food

Actually, mosquitoes do not bite at all. The female, which is the blood drinker, first probes the surface of the skin and then inserts a slender, needle-like tube into a blood vessel, injecting a fluid that blocks the blood from clotting as she sips. It is this little dose

Mosquito mouth, magnified 9 times

of spit-like liquid that causes the swelling and itching in your skin. It is also this liquid that sneaks terrible diseases from the mosquito into her prey, including human malaria, various forms of bird malaria, yellow fever, elephantiasis, dengue fever, and dog heartworm. Fortunately, in Hawaiʻi, the mosquito does not transmit human diseases.

The female can suck in her own weight in blood until her bulging body is fully bloated. Then she slowly balloons away and digests her valuable blood load. The male mosquito does not feed on blood, but probably drinks in the tiny secretions of sap that appear at the limb and twig joints of plants. The life histories of many insects—even such common ones as the mosquito—are not fully understood. It may be that the male mosquito lives off body fat, thereby accomplishing his biological tasks.

Habitat

Mosquitoes thrive in the moist air and lush foliage of our woods and forests, where wind can't batter their frail, sailing flight. They lay their eggs in standing water, and with water so plentiful in old Hawaiʻi and very few natural predators, mosquitoes bred in swarms and quickly became a serious irritation. For some years, island school children were enlisted in "mosquito fighting brigades" and rewarded for retrieving cans or jars in which stagnant water might collect.

Just Wondering

With such a hospitable habitat for mosquito breeding, it is a wonder that Hawaiʻi does not suffer from any of the mosquito-borne human diseases: dengue, encephalitis, malaria. How has Hawaiʻi managed to avoid these diseases?

Reproduction

Male mosquitoes usually live only two to three weeks and die shortly after mating. Females can live several months and breed repeatedly. In cold climates, females survive winter, laying eggs in the spring. It is quite possible that a female mosquito with fertile eggs made the crossing from North America to Hawaiʻi on a visiting ship.

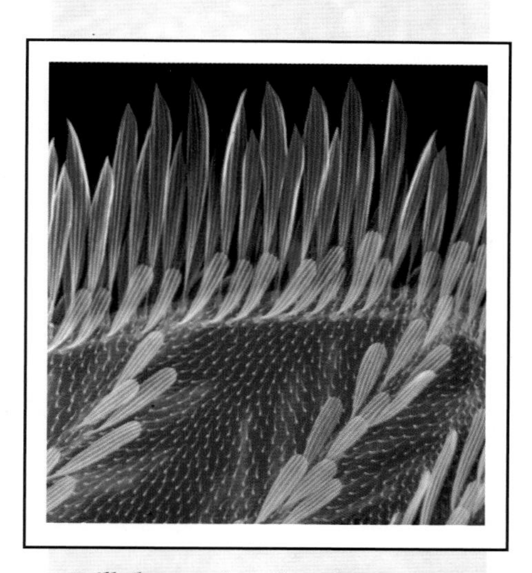

Frilled mosquito wing edge, magnified 300 times

The tiny shrill whine of the mosquito is actually a high-frequency ring produced by the rapid vibrations of its wings as it nears your ear. The female mosquito's wings beat more slowly than the male's, and it is thought that the lower rate of ringing helps the male locate her before mating. He uses his feathery feelers, called antennae, in detecting what he may sense as her slower whine.

A rich blood meal is necessary as a source of nutrients for the development of her eggs, two to three hundred of which are enveloped in a water-repellent capsule called a raft and laid on

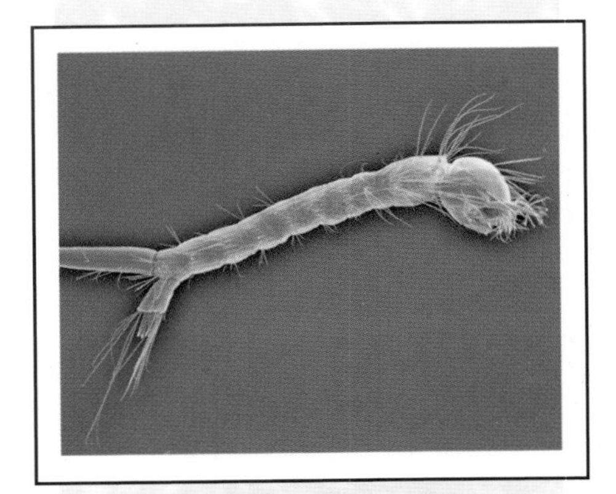

Mosquito wriggler, magnified 5 times

the surface of standing water. The larvae hatch directly into the water through a tiny trapdoor underneath this raft. Legless, wingless wrigglers are nearly invisible in their hairy paleness. The skin is shed several times as their bodies grow and darken. Made buoyant by their bristly body hair, the wrigglers feed on microscopic plants and animals and spend much of their time floating at the surface. They draw air through the surface film by way of a breathing straw. Their prickly hairs provide some protection from many enemies.

Within a week, wrigglers change to comma-shaped, big-headed pupae. These are nonfeeders, spending their time at the surface breathing through two air tubes, little horns protruding from the back of their heads. The forming mosquito body shows as a dark outline within the brownish case. When disturbed, the pupae jump to the murky bottom in jerky, jack-knifing movements.

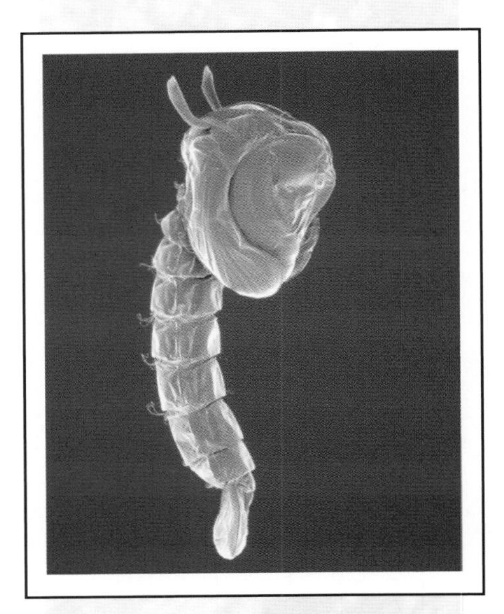

Mosquito pupa, magnified 4 times

In a few days, the formed mosquito is ready to hatch, a process that will take about five minutes. The pupa flattens out its body on the surface of the water. Air is pumped into the pupal casing, causing it to float up higher in the water. As the skin swells, a seam along the top splits. The mosquito slowly works itself out, first pushing up its back and head. Its antennae and wings lift up and it steps out of the case, one leg at a time. Briefly it remains standing on the clear, cellophane-like casing while its body hardens and wings stiffen.

Then it is off, whirring away in search of a mate or a meal.

Just Wondering

Insect species outnumber those of all other creatures in the animal kingdom by an estimated ten to one. Three factors are generally given to explain their success: their ability to fly, the process of metamorphosis they pass through as they develop and their shielding exoskeleton. These factors give them enormous adaptability as they meet conditions on Earth. How so?

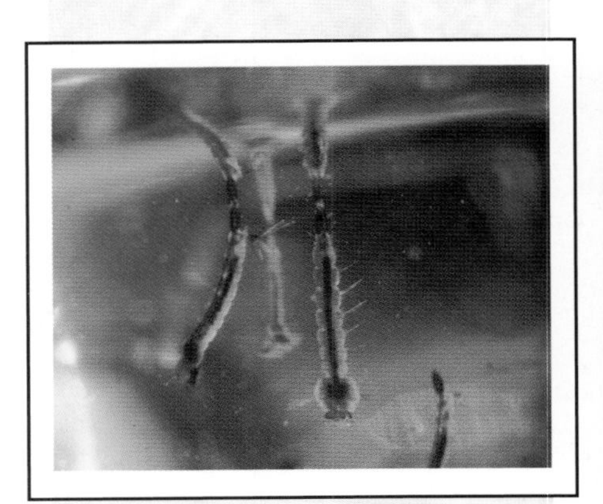

Bristly wrigglers dangle in standing water.

A mosquito slides out of its pupal casing. In minutes its body stiffens and it is ready for flight.

More Mosquito Facts

Bird malaria and avian pox are carried to endemic Hawaiian birds in the mouths of mosquitoes. No one is quite sure when Hawaiian birds first developed the grotesque leg and face swellings that characterize avian pox. Reports from Kona on the island of Hawai'i and from O'ahu began to appear in the 1890s. One thought is that introduced cage birds brought these diseases to the islands and, with the arrival of the new culex type of mosquito, the pox viruses and lethal protozoa were carried deep into native forests to unprotected birds. The damp habitat of the Hawaiian crow makes it particularly vulnerable to attack by disease-carrying mosquitoes, while the *kōlea*, at home in open, windswept spaces, seems better protected. What's more, in their annual travels abroad, the *kōlea* were probably exposed to these diseases and, over time, acquired resistance.

»»»»»»»»»

As more and more native birds fell silent to disease and habitat destruction, humans began to import a variety of replacement species. Newspapers published warnings against the killing of these birds and added threats of fines to assure their becoming established in the islands:

»»»»»»»» Views »»»»»»»»

"New Birds Restricted—Dr. Hillebrand came to our offices to request that we announce publicly that it is prohibited to shoot the introduced birds that may have been observed recently. A number of these birds resemble carrier pigeons in size. Therefore, with the publication of this warning, take heed, for anyone who violates it will be fined $50. This does not only apply to **kānakas** ***but to*** **haoles** ***as well. Every effort should be made to follow this law. Therefore, take heed and cease your wishful thinking or there will be a high price to pay."***

(Nūpepa Kū'oko'a, *March, 1867, trans. author)*

The killing of *kōlea* was outlawed during the 1860s as sugar planters realized their usefulness in controlling army-worm infestations in the growing sugar industry. Hawaiians, deprived of a delicious and traditional treat, turned their hunting skills and eating pleasures to the recently introduced mynah:

»»»»»»»» Views »»»»»»»»

"Concerning Introduced Birds—There are numerous hunter enthusiasts wanting to shoot birds in our fields here, however they should beware of the Indian Miners [sic], brought here from abroad. A fine of $50 will be assessed anyone who unlawfully shoots such a bird. These birds in large part are now in Moanalua, and persons have been mistaken in thinking they are crows. Therefore, let it be remembered that there is a high price to pay for anyone shooting introduced birds."

(Nūpepa Kū'oko'a, *February, 1868, trans. author)*

Many kinds of animals have been introduced to Hawai'i over the years to eat mosquitoes and their wrigglers, including the bufo, the poison dart frog, several kinds of birds and an assortment of fish, among them the guppy, mosquito fish and swordtail. All of these fish are now common in our streams; they entered the islands with a costly environmental price tag:

»»»»»»»» *Views* »»»»»»»»

"The lowlands used to teem with certain delicate and beautiful native damselflies. After the introductions of fresh-water fishes such as top minnows, the native damselflies, whose ancestors never had to protect themselves from fishes, became scarce."

(E.C. Zimmerman, 1948)

In 1929, the first of three cannibal mosquitoes was brought in to battle the human-biting species by attacking its wrigglers. There are now eight mosquito species in Hawai'i, all introduced by humans.

»»»»»»»»

Scientists are able to calculate an insect's per-second wing-beat rate. As a rule, the smaller the insect the greater the number of wing strokes per second. Compare, for example, the low-pitched buzz of the black carpenter bee (150 beats per second), the hum of the honeybee (250 beats per second), and the piercing ring of the mosquito (500–600 beats per second.) By comparison, a sparrow's wings beat about 17 times per second and the blink of the human eye takes about $^{1}/_{25}$ of a second.

»»»»»» *Just Wondering* »»»»»»

How does such a beautiful thing as a wing evolve?

Mosquitoes are easily raised in a glass jar, which provides good viewing of their stages of development, or metamorphosis. Keep in mind that if an adult female escapes, she will immediately seek out a tasty blood meal—which will likely be you!

Large red damselfly, a native Hawaiian gnat catcher. Males fearlessly patrol breeding territory in streams, where the naiads (immature stage, photo left) eat aquatic insects, but are themselves devoured by alien released aquarium fishes. Forest sister species lay eggs near leaf axil water of certain endemic plants.

To find you, she uses an impressive system of insect technology. She can gauge the level of carbon dioxide in the air around her and, in detecting an increase, zero in on you. She can also register levels of heat and moisture coming from your skin, and these will lead her straight to you.

Just Wondering

Is the mosquito's ability to detect a warm-blooded animal the same thing as a sense of smell? A dog has 200 million smell receptor cells; a human has 5 million. Can a fish smell? Can a bird smell? How does the smell of baking chocolate-chip cookies travel from a windless kitchen to your closed bedroom with such incredible speed?

In the days of our grandparents, schoolchildren were frequently enlisted in pest elimination campaigns. Mosquitoes and rats were the main targets of these efforts. Cashing in cans and bottles brought a bit of pocket change to island kids and rid backyards of wriggler water. A newspaper report from 1946 reminded young readers there was also money to be made from rat tails:

Views

"PRICES FOR RAT TAILS IN KONA ADVANCE TO 3 CENTS; DRIVE ON

Rat tail prices in Kona have gone up. Last year the Kona Coffee Leaders Association paid school children a bounty of two cents per tail during Kona's annual rat extermination drive. This year they are paying 3 cents. The rat drive, now in full swing, will end June 28 . . . . Every Friday is rat bounty day in these schools. On this day the youngsters turn their week's accumulation of rat tails into cash."

(The Honolulu Advertiser, *March 24, 1946*)

The Internet is a-buzz with more than a thousand mosquito sites. Check 'em out!

NA MAKIKA

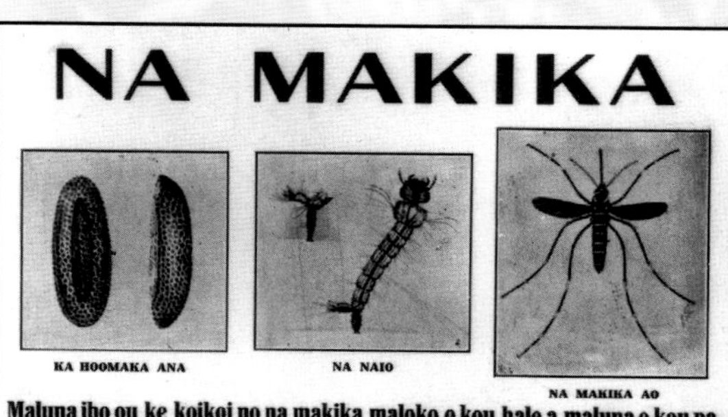

Maluna iho ou ke koikoi no na makika maloko o kou hale a maluna o kou pa

E heluhelu i keia mau mea mahope ae nei me ke akahele loa, aole wale no nae e heluhelu ia mea aka e nana pu maluna o ia mea.

1. Iloko wale no o ka wai e hanau ai ka makika; o ka mea maa ma ka wai hou, na wai hooki'o ma na wahi i hanaia.
2. O kekahi mau wahi e hoopulapula ai na makika o ia no keia malalo iho nei: Na wahi hooki'o o na wai ino, na lua hoahu, na tini, na omole, a i ole kekahi mau mea e ae e lana ai ka wai.
3. E oili ae ana na makika makahi a lakou i hoopulapula ai. Aole e hiki ia lakou ke holopapa aku ma na wahi mamao.
4. O ka makika opiopio "ke naio" e noho ana ia iloko o ka wai ma kahi o ka 10 a 12 la.
5. Oiai e noho ana na naio iloko o ka wai, he mea pono ia lakou e oili mau ae iluna o ka ili wai no ka hanu ana.
6. O ka aila e lana ana iluna o ka wai, ka mea nana e pale aku i na naio mai ka hanu ana.
7. E hoopoino aku i na wahi e hoopulapula ai o na makika, e pau auanei na makika.
8. E ninini i ka wai mailoko aku o na kapu, na pakeke, na tini, na ipu pua, na pahu, na holowaa wai, etc., he hookahi manawa iloko o kela eha a elima paha la. E hoomaemae i na hawai o kou hale i kela ame keia pule a e makaala ina ua loaa ka lawa i na paipu e holo ana ilalo no ka lawe ana aku i ka wai, a he hi-o hoi ko na hawai, e hiki ole ai ke lana ka wai. He oi loa aku nae ka pono, ina aole he hawai.
9. E hoopiha a i ole e hoomaloo i na ki'owai, na wahi i eliia, na auwai, a i ole na wahi halua apau.
10. E hoolooliloli mau i kela ame keia eha a i ole elima la i ka wai i makemakeia maloko o na pa moa, na hale ilio, a i ole na holowaa no ka hoohainu ana i ka holoholona.
11. E ninini i ka aila mahu i na wai halana e hiki ole ana ke hunaia a i ole hoomalooia (I auneki o ka aila ua lawa ia no ka uhi ana i ka ili o 15 kapuai kuea). Aole e lilo ka aila i mea hoopoino mai i ka wai no ka hoohana ana aku ina malalo e laweia mai ai. Ina ne nui loa ka iliaina no ka ninini ana aku i ka aila a i ole hiki ole paha ke hoomalooia e hookomo aku i ka i'a ai makika (top minnows) iloko o ia mea.
12. E uhi i na luawai me na upena uwea, na luawai ame na kula wai e hoohana mauia ana i kela ame keia la.
13. O na wahi i makemake oleia e nininiia me ka aila, ua hiki no ke hoopakeleia mai na makika aku ina e hookomoia aku ana ka i'a ai makika a i'a gula paha.
14. E nana pono ina paha aole he mau wahi i pilikia o na paipu. E hoopaa aku i na wahi kulu o na paipu a i ole na wahi paa paha o na hawai.
15. E nana pono i na wahi hooki'o o na wai ino, ina paha ua paa ko lakou mau pani a ua uhiia na puka o na paipu e kahe aku ai iloko o ka luawai. E aila i na lua liilii i kela ame keia eha la.
16. E hukihuki i na nahelehele apau, na mauu, honohono ame na laalaau ma na wahi i eliia, na loko ame kekahi mau wahi kupono e ae no ka makika e hoopulapula ai, oiai he mau wahi ia no na makika nunui e pee ai.
17. E hoomaemae i na pa waiho wale ame na pa mahope mai na tini mai, na omole ame ka opala. E poke a okioki i na laau kiwala-o.
18. O ka mua e hoopau aku i na wahi apau i ikeia he mau wahi lakou no ka hoopulapula ana o na makika, alaila hoomaka aku ka hana ma na wahi e hiki ai ia lakou ke hoopulapula hou ole aku.
19. Oiai he makaainana oe no kou puulu iho, he mea pono e loaa ia oe ka manao no ke kau ana aku o ke koikoi maluna ou e hoopau aku i ka hoolahaia ana o ka makika maloko o kou apana, a e hui pu aku ma ka hana like ana me kou mau hoa noho, i wahi e pau ai na wahi hoopulapula o na makika. E hele aku e nana pono a e ninini aku i ka aila mahu i na hawai, na wahi halua, na lua i eliia, na lua liilii, na wahi hooki'o wai, etc., ma ka pili alanui.
20. Ma kahi o ka aila i nininiia i na wai halana he mea pono ke ninini likeia maluna o ka iliwai me ka paa pono o ka iliwai holookoa i ka uhiia.
21. He pono na hale apau loa e kaawale mai na makika eheu aku, ma ke puhiia ana o ka pauda makika. E haule iho ana na makika iluna o ka papahele a e houluuluia ae a puhi aku i ke ahi.
22. Mai kaukai wale no maluna o ka aila i wahi e pau ai ka makika, e hoopoino pu i na wahi e hoopunana ai na makika a e hoomaloo i na wai halana apau. E hana aku me ka pauaho ole e like me ka hiki.
23. O ka maha e loaa ana i kekahi puulu a i kekahi apana paha ua kaukaiia aku ia maluna o ka hana like ana o kela ame keia lala o ia puulu.

Turn-of-the-century poster in Hawaiian alerts readers to mosquito menace and provides information about its reproductive cycle and about ridding the yard of breeding sites.

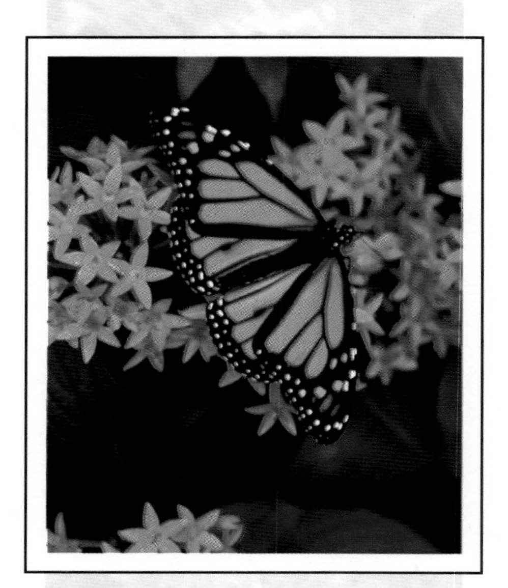

Hawaiian name: *Lepelepe-o-Hina*
Scientific Name: *Danaus plexippus*
Area of Origin: North America
Date of Arrival: Early 1800s (?)

LEAF TO WING

The Monarch Butterfly

ARRIVAL IN HAWAIʻI

Perhaps an autumn storm blew a few butterflies far west off course and landed them in Hawaiʻi. Or a monarch butterfly may have clung to a sailing ship's riggings as a stowaway. But it was only from the early 1800s that monarchs found a permanent food source in Hawaiʻi—the introduced crown flower of the milkweed family.

HABITAT

This orange-black butterfly originally evolved in the fields and forests of North America. From there, over time, it flew and floated or was boated to all continents of the world, where its food, the milkweed plant, grew. Like the *kōlea*, the North American monarch migrates between different types of habitat, thus assuring its needs as a species.

American observers are amazed by these autumn migrations, when millions of monarchs fly off into a two-thousand-mile journey south. Some years ago a game warden in the state of Washington noticed what he thought was a huge dark cloud moving southward. As it approached, it proved instead to be countless butterflies in a gigantic glittering blur that he estimated to be ten to fifteen miles long.

Flying south, the monarchs flee the descending north cold—the cold that kills their eggs, larvae and pupae. Those summering in the western United States fly to Southern California; those in the eastern part of the continent fly south, their destination the same wintering location each year—a small, sloping, twenty-acre stand of fir trees in Mexico.

Just Wondering

As with the amazing homing instincts of the honu *that returns to the sands of its birth, and the young* kōlea *that wings its way to specks of islands it has never before visited, scientists cannot explain the accuracy with which these butterflies navigate their route back to a location some twenty-five hundred miles away that they have never known. How can they know? Follow the leader?*

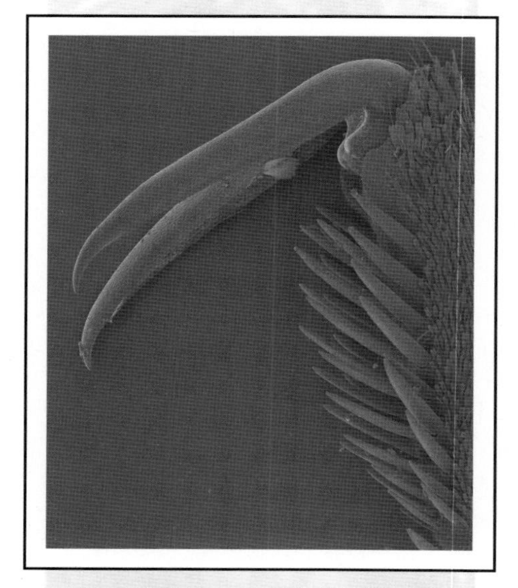

Monarch foot, magnified 4 times; terminal spikes may be used to scrape leaf surface. Bristly sensors below are sensitive to chemicals.

From November to late January clumps of butterflies blanket the trees, their hinged wings clamped shut in a semisleep that conserves energy for the return flight north.

With February sun warming woods and wings, the firs burst

ablaze with the flickerings of millions of orange and silvery-black butterflies. The monarchs flit northward—this time individually—laying their eggs and refilling the world with their fluttering fragile beauty.

Just Wondering

What is the difference between a moth and a butterfly?

Food

Because of the evenly warm temperatures in Hawai'i, monarchs do not migrate, and the crown flower, which produces a thick, milky sap so very poisonous to most other animals, including humans, grows year-round.

Monarch caterpillars, like the cockroach and termite, feed by moving their jaws sideways, not up and down. The adult, however, lacks the typical double set of jaws of these insects, so it never chews. A butterfly's slender, coiling "tongue," called a proboscis, allows it to drink in food only by sipping nectar from flowers. To locate food, butterflies use their feet. They can recognize even a very weak mixture of honey or sugar in water by wetting their feet. They also locate the right food plant on which to lay their eggs by thumping lightly on a leaf to identify its "flavor."

Just Wondering

Many flowers turn with the sun as it moves over the sky. No feet, no wheels, no "mouse" to click on twice, and no eyes, noses or necks. How do flowers do it?

Reproduction

The male and female monarch meet in a fluttering dance, curving higher and higher in curling circles for several seconds. The male, passing ahead as they spiral upward, puts out a faint perfume to her like that of flowers: a special spot on each of his hind wings has scales that are attached to scent glands. The delicate honeysuckle fragrance is hardly discernible to the human nose but is attractive to her. It's a clear signal that identifies him unmistakably as the right species for her to mate with. They tumble clumsily to the ground or to a crown flower leaf, where they mate. During mating, the scent of the male surrounds the female, and what seems to be the close fragrance of flowers causes her "tongue" to coil and uncoil.

Just Wondering

The spiral is one of the basic shapes of nature, found in the microscopic blueprint of life called DNA, in the graceful strength of the spider web and in the coiled ram's horn. What other spirals are described in this book? What advantages might be found in the coiled shape of the spiral?

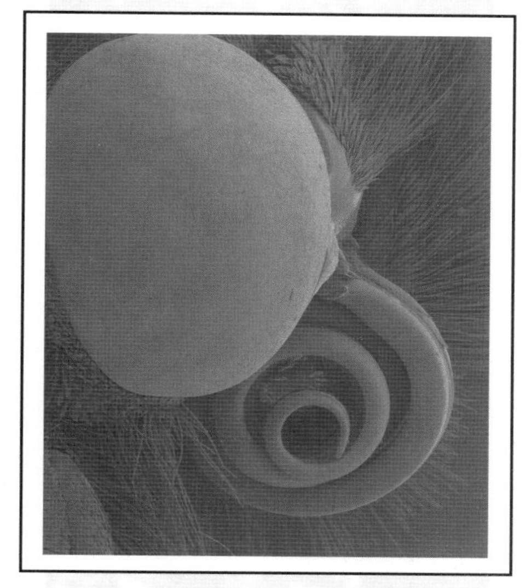

Monarch proboscis, magnified 20 times

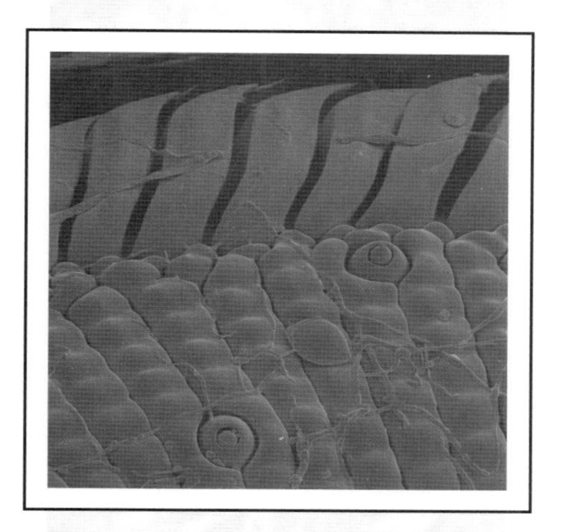

Monarch proboscis, magnified 600 times; note rounded scent glands.

Crown flower in bloom

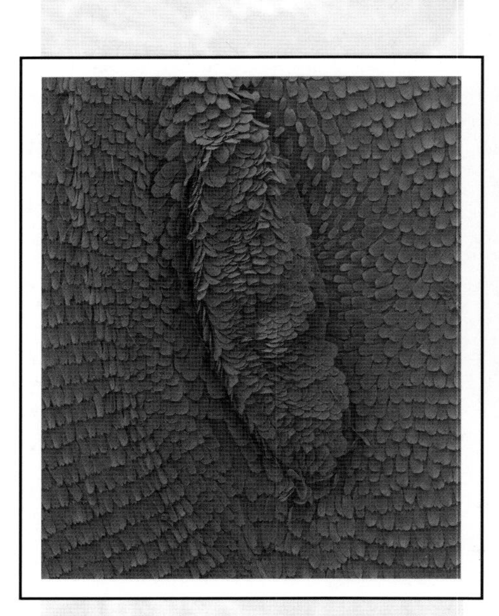

Scent gland on male wing, magnified 35 times

A first day of caterpillar munchings

The female now flutters from leaf to leaf, setting a single fertilized egg here and there on the host plant. Insect eggs, unlike those of the *kōlea* or *honu*, have very little yolk. Thus the female must place her eggs near an immediate source of food for her offspring. She dots a speck of pale green beneath the large lime-colored leaf of the crown flower, which will serve both as cradle and first meal. This egg is the beginning of four distinct stages in the development of the new monarch.

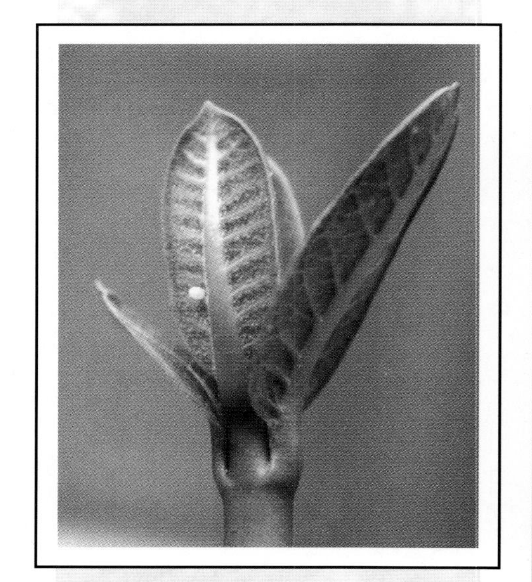

Egg on crown flower leaf

Monarch caterpillar: metamorphosis, step two

Within three days the egg hatches; a tiny, sixteen-legged caterpillar appears and promptly gobbles up the egg case that had held it, recycling the little sack as a first snack. The real food, however, is the fuzzy leaf underfoot: carving downward with its sharp jaws, the caterpillar cuts curved slices of leaf at a rapid pace as it continues its feeding in an endless meal. Munching milkweed, it grows quickly, storing up juices and tissues that will soon transform to stunning butterfly grace. Leaving lace in place of leaves, it excretes pungent green clumps behind as it gnaws away at leaf after leaf.

The caterpillar's growth is quick for a dozen or so days, during which time its skin—now a brightly striped black, yellow and green—splits and molts several times. It is soon nearly two inches long and ready to pass to the third stage of its metamorphosis: the pupa.

Finding a branch or the underside of a leaf, the caterpillar spins a small tab of silk from its mouth, attaches its tail, then drops down in a fishhook shape. It hangs nearly motionless for several hours, except for an occasional slight twitch, which indicates that inside it is actively preparing for change.

Then suddenly its skin splits. The writhing caterpillar twists the skin upward and off its body. Magically, the larva is no more. In its place, and hanging perfectly still, is a pale green chrysalis. A *lei* of rich gold speckles the cap like a tiny monarch's crown.

Tight and clear as a Ziploc bag, the casing quickly dries around the smooth, waxy chrysalis. In Hawaiian warmth, growth is quick. In days to come, the capsule hardens and darkens as the butterfly's orange-and-black color deepens and its form shows through the transparent pupa case. The undeveloped wings, dimly outlined, hang like hands in prayer.

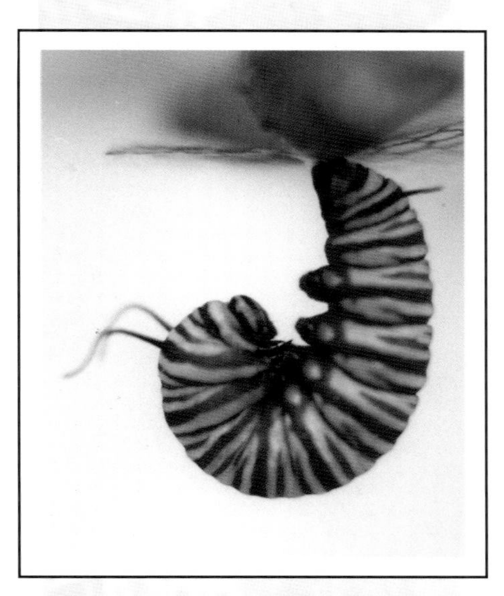

Hanging in a hook shape . . .

Just Wondering

During the caterpillar's days as a chrysalis, its fourteen segments, with sixteen legs, four antennae and munching mouth, seem as if by magic to dissolve and reform to the three segments, six legs, two wings and proboscis of a butterfly! How to explain such magic?

suddenly it twists back its striped skin.

Within a week the monarch emerges from its chamber. Its clumsy, bloated body and stumped, crumpled wings, however, are far from flight. Clinging to a leaf or twig, the butterfly begins to pump out blood from its heart. Gradually, the four shriveled

A chrysalis takes form.

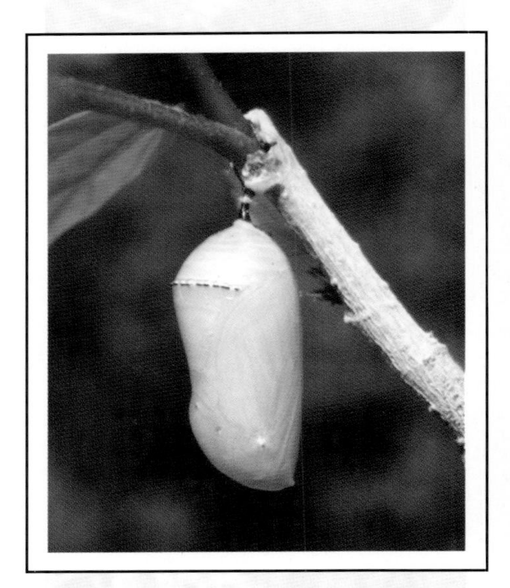

As though made of jade, a crowned chrysalis

Stunning butterfly transformation

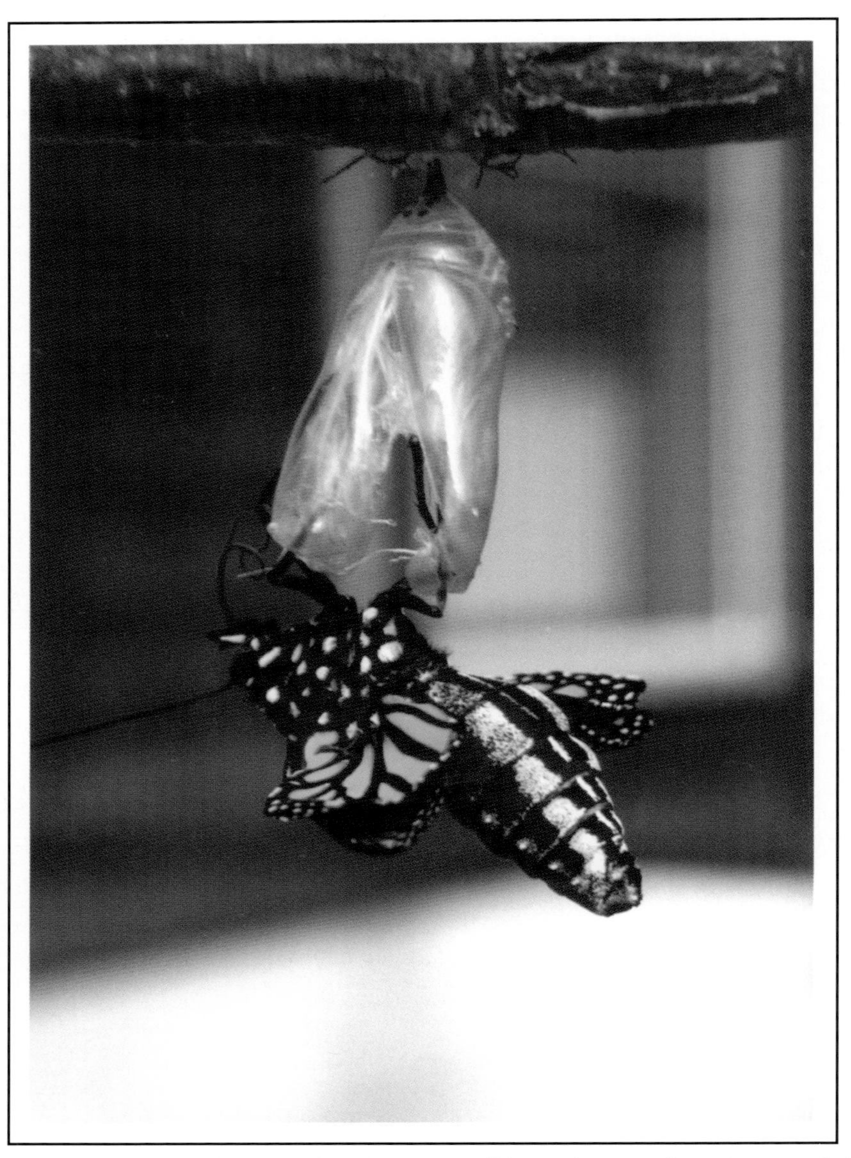

The butterfly is swollen with fluid that soon will be used to stretch out its crumpled wings.

wings extend, stretch and become pliant like little colored kites; its body grows firm as its exoskeleton hardens. The butterfly waits and rests, slowly uncoiling and recoiling its proboscis, or "tongue," slowly opening and closing its wings.

Then, light as sunlight, with an abrupt and silent flutter of its stiff wings, it lifts and flits off.

Just Wondering

Unlike birds, which spend much of their flying time sailing through the air on fixed, outstretched wings, insects fly by flapping their wings continuously. The monarch butterfly is one of the very few insects that will slide into a glide as it flies. Why don't insects lock their wings into a sailing, sliding stiffness?

More Monarch Butterfly Facts

Scales on monarch wing, magnified 500 times

The brilliant orange-and-black wings of the monarch clearly advertise a message of warning to insect-eating birds. This is very different from the protective tone displayed by the changing colorations of the gecko's skin or the plain markings of the *kōlea* egg. The bright colors of the monarch blink danger to an approaching stranger. For a dozen days as a caterpillar, it fed on the toxic tissues and juices of the milkweed plant, accumulating enough sickening poison to kill a small bird. Occasionally, a bird is seen gobbling down a caterpillar, only to vomit it right back up. In Hawai'i such insect eaters as the red-crested bulbul sometimes swerve toward the monarch, then veer off suddenly, perhaps "warned" by the bright wing patterns. Scientists believe that the toxin is accumulated in the million or so scales that cover the monarch's body.

Just Wondering

Though a bird has only twenty-five taste buds on its tongue, it still reacts immediately to the bitter poison of the monarch caterpillar. Humans begin life with about ten thousand taste buds, but these decline in number with years, leaving the mouth with as few as three thousand in old age. So how does the declining number of taste buds in humans relate to the fact that onions, spinach, garlic and mushrooms are generally despised foods in childhood but become much appreciated by adults?

February sunshine in the Sierra Madre mountains of Mexico stirs monarchs from their slumber on winter firs. Mexicans say that the hushed sound of wing rustlings is the whispering of saints. The butterflies sail off quietly northward, eleven fluttering miles an hour, eighty fluttering miles a day, seeding milkweed plants with eggs as they pass. Eventually, wings tatter and butterflies die. Their offspring continue the northward flight, dotting down eggs as they go. In turn they die and their young fly on up into the northeastern part of the United States. Wave upon wave of butterflies replace each other as they go north with spring. The final butterflies—perhaps fourth- or fifth-generation descendants of those that wintered in Mexico—reach far north into eastern Canada. When autumn returns, their offspring begin the trip back to Mexico—to that same small stand of Oyamel fir trees high in the Sierra Madre. Unfortunately, the stand of firs that shelters them in winter is being eyed by timber cutters. If the trees are cut down, the unique microclimate created there may be lost and with it the millions of butterflies that dapple summer fields and apple orchards of North America.

Just Wondering

Why does it take four to five butterfly generations for the trek north but only one for the trek south?

Check out the monarch migration on these websites:
http://www.monarchwatch.org/ or
http://www.pacificgrove.com/butterflies or
http://www.learner.org/jnorth/

The monarch butterfly is host specific. Its caterpillar's food source is the milkweed—the crown flower in Hawai'i—without which it cannot survive. Countless endemic Hawaiian species are also dependent on a single host plant. With the arrival of foreign livestock, which grazed and trampled out much of the endemic flora, many insect species have been lost, most of them before they were ever identified by scientists:

Views

"Each native plant in Hawai'i supports a lesser or greater assemblage of associated insects. Many insects are absolutely host specific. When their host plants become restricted in range, the range of the insects shrinks accordingly. Deforestation and extermination of various trees of our islands have accounted for the extinction of an untold number of associated insects. Some insects which were at one time abundant on certain trees back of Honolulu are now no longer found, because, for many years, we have been unable to find a specimen of their host plants."

(E.C. Zimmerman, 1948)

Kamehameha butterfly

An endemic Hawaiian butterfly that resembles the monarch is called the Kamehameha butterfly. Its host plant is also a milkweed, the native *māmaki.* The young caterpillar of this species creates a shelter by gnawing out a flap of the *māmaki* leaf, rolling it over its body, and attaching it back to the leaf. It then gnaws on the leaf in the protection of its little tent. Older caterpillars spin a chrysalis that resembles a wilted *māmaki* leaf as it hangs nearly undetectable on the host plant.

Until 1972, it was generally assumed that all butterfly and moth caterpillars ate only green leaves and other plant material. That year, in a remarkable discovery on the island of Hawai'i, a scientist found Hawaiian caterpillars that wait in ambush for flies. This is an extraordinary example of how species evolve over time in unique ways within a given habitat. Often similar in color to the habitat in which they are found, these little caterpillars lie along a leaf edge or twig until prey alights. Hairs on the caterpillar's hind end act as sensors: the strike is immediate. The inchworm flicks out its stubby claws and clasps the

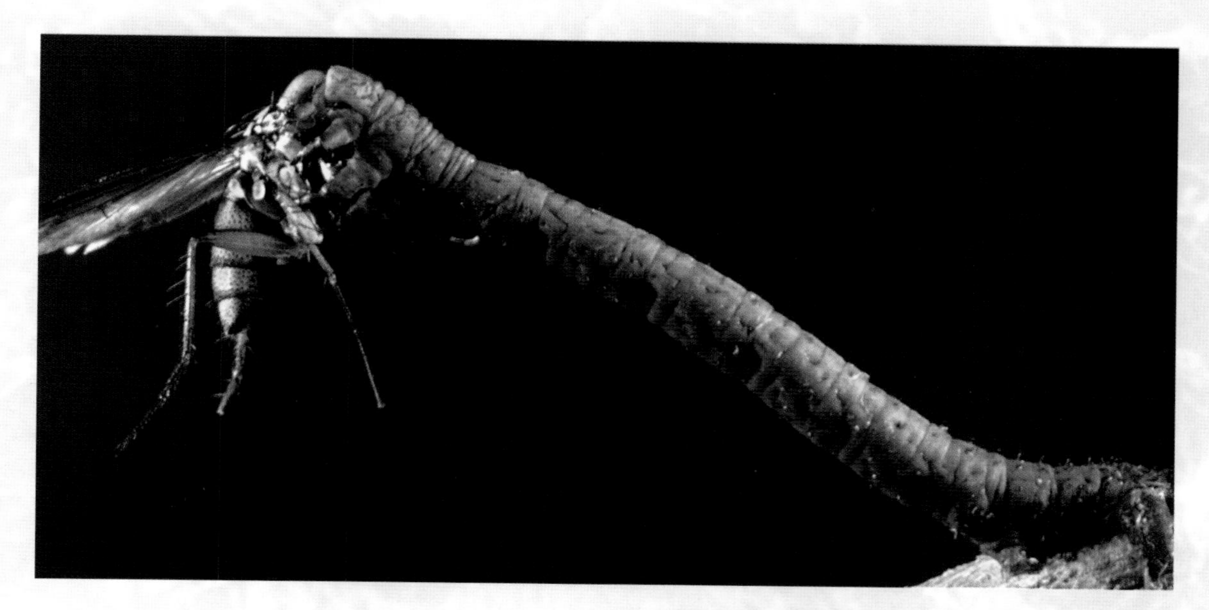

insect like a closed fist. Of the more than one hundred thousand known caterpillars in the world, the Hawaiian species are the only examples of carnivores that ambush their prey.

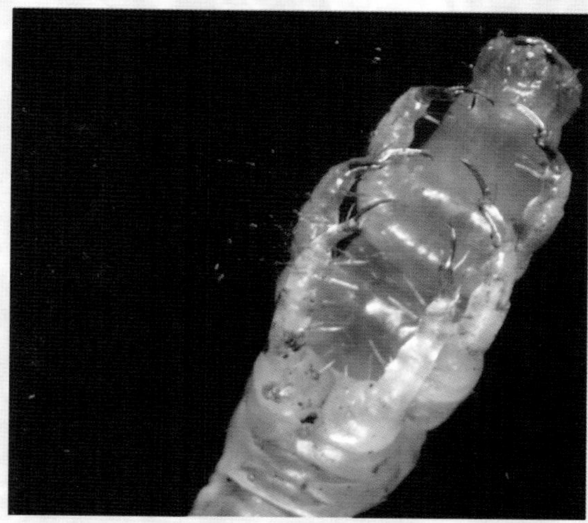

The presence of eighteen ambushing inchworm species in Hawai'i is quite stunning in the world of insects. Using a "sit-and-wait" strategy, the caterpillars lie on leaves, twigs, ferns and the forest floor, capturing prey with lightning speed (top). The caterpillars mature as nectar-drinking moths. Bottom photo is a close up, bug-eye view of the caterpillar's six long claws and foreleg spines, all held like a basket to snatch victims in a 1/10-second strike.

Just Wondering

Is it possible that the toxicity of the monarch butterfly contributed to the die-off of native bird species that did not "know" the monarch was poisonous?

Views

"But most of all I shall remember the monarchs, that unhurried westward drift of one small winged form after another, each drawn by some invisible force. Did they return? We thought not; for most at least, this was the closing journey of their lives."

(Rachel Carson, source unknown)

FARMING KAPI'OLANI PARK

The Ostrich

By 1850, as hundreds of ships made their way yearly to and from the Hawaiian Islands, countless alien animals and plants were coming in, sometimes intentionally, often accidentally, sometimes to establish permanent populations, more often to die and be gone. Honolulu, as the main port city, was filling with trees, shrubs and flowers that had never before grown in these islands. Cattle, goats and sheep, released from the earliest foreign ships, were running in huge herds on several of the neighbor islands, blanketing vast tracts of country and stripping land of its protective vegetation. Delicate Hawaiian tree snails, once so plentiful, were no longer seen near the sea. Soft and crunchy grasshoppers that for centuries had been collected for food by children off the morning shrubs of Ka'ū on the Big Island were vanishing as the only plant they fed on became a favored food of rampaging cattle and goats. Today, many of our islands, particularly Lāna'i, Kaho'olawe, Moloka'i, and Kaua'i, still show the scars of excessive grazing.

Hawaiian Name: *'Akolika*
Scientific Name: *Struthio camelus*
Area of Origin: Africa
Date of Arrival: 1890

Sheepherding, Mauna Kea, island of Hawai'i, late 1800s

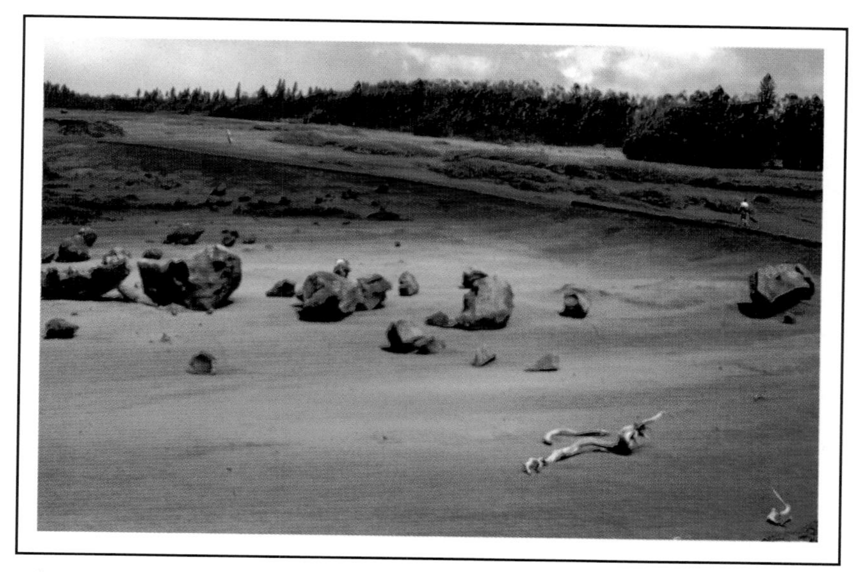

This raw, red landscape on the island of Lāna'i is the result of damage by cattle, wind, rain and deer.

Hawaiian birds were retreating farther and farther into mountain forests as foreign birds like the mynah, rice bird, house finch, and many kinds of game birds took over the lowlands. Both Hawaiian and English newspapers repeated warnings to *kānaka* and *haole* alike not to kill the imported birds, or be fined heavily. The wetlands, now planted in rice instead of taro, were infested with mosquitoes. Avian malaria, carried silently in the mouths of mosquitoes, took swelling and death inland to what remained of the unique Hawaiian birds.

Arrival in Hawai'i

The ostrich is one of many different kinds of animals that people attempted to introduce to Hawai'i but that didn't establish a permanent population. Among all the failed introductions, the ostrich is a particularly noteworthy example. Nobody knows what happened to Mr. Taner's emu, an Australian cousin of the ostrich, mentioned in the article below as the first such bird to arrive in Hawai'i:

Views

"Mr. Taner brought from Australia an Australian ostrich or emu, a pair of black swans, a kangaroo rat and a pair of white rabbits, as well as a variety of plants and shrubs, some are new at the islands. The introduction of new animals, plants, etc. by residents returning from their visits to other countries is highly praiseworthy and commendable and we hope persons visiting foreign countries and returning will bear in mind that they can thus contribute to the general good of the islands by the introduction of many things that will contribute to the pleasure or profit of themselves or the residents generally."

(The Polynesian, *October 22, 1853*)

 *Just Wondering*

A state law in Hawaiʻi requires the use of Hawaiian words on all new street signs. The purpose of this law is to try to keep Hawaiʻi Hawaiian. How about a law requiring that native species be used any time a public works project needs to put in trees and plants? Wouldn't that be "highly praiseworthy and commendable?"

Several newspapers carried articles about this unusual flightless bird, and interest grew in establishing ostriches in the islands. In the late 1800s, the ornamental value of ostrich feathers soared when the connoisseurs of Paris, London and New York determined their fashion appeal as the preferred decoration on ladies' hats. It was at this time that a Frenchman named Dr. George Trousseau, a physician in service to the Hawaiian monarchy, decided to set up an ostrich farm at Kapiʻolani Park on Oʻahu.

Three ostriches were ordered from California at a hefty cost of $1,000 each, and Trousseau's Hawaiian Ostrich Farm Company got its start in June of 1890. One of the two females, however, was injured during the trip over and died shortly after arrival in Honolulu.

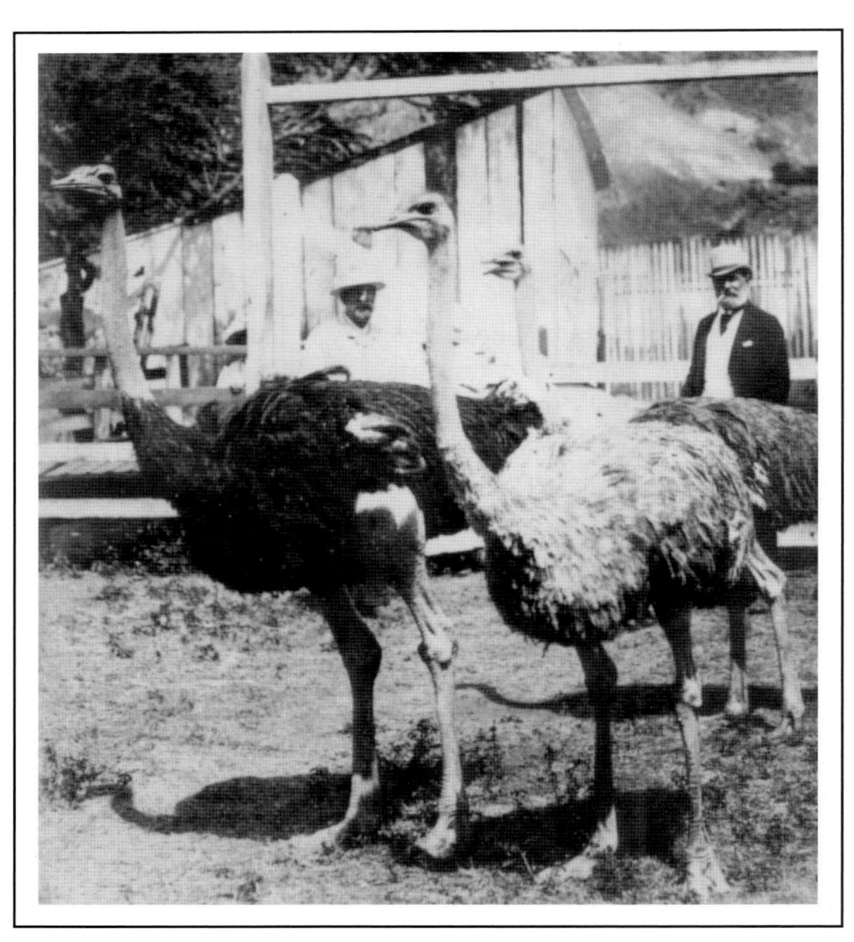

Trousseau's ostriches

One thousand dollars was a tremendous sum of money in June of 1890. That same month a subscription to the *Daily Bulletin*, a major newspaper published every morning, was fifty cents per month. Nine acres of good land in Pālolo Valley just *ma uka* of Honolulu was selling for $10,000, and the Bishop Estate was willing to lease eight hundred acres of its land at Wa'ahila, O'ahu, for an annual fee of $200.

Habitat

The barren fields on the *ma kai* side of Diamond Head were—before the days of hoses and sprinklers—quite similar to the dry habitat where ostriches evolved, and thus suited the foraging habits of these birds. In their African homeland, ostriches are frequently observed grazing together on open and dusty plains with zebras, antelopes and other herd animals.

Food

The ostriches of Waikīkī grazed on grass and leaves that make up their diet as well as the new shoots of the young *kiawe* trees that to this day still stand in Kapi'olani Park near the present site of the Honolulu Zoo. Ostriches also eagerly gobble up insects and lizards they happen upon. Like chickens and pigeons, they use little stones that break down their food as part of digestion.

On July 24 of that year, just a month after the arrival of Trousseau's birds, the first ostrich egg was found in the fields of Kap'iolani, causing quite a stir in the local press and attracting a stream of gawking sightseers to view the oddity. Families planned their weekend outings to visit the Hawaiian Ostrich Farm and get a glimpse of these strange birds and their first hatchling.

Donkey-drawn trolley, late 1800s

Nineteen chicks hatched in 1891, and within two years there were thirty Hawai'i-born ostriches strutting the plain of Kapi'olani together with several hundred cackling chickens of the finest breed. As unlikely as it now may seem, high-quality Hawaiian ostrich feathers were fetching fancy prices as far away as London.

Reproduction

The male ostrich is very active in showing off in the mating game. His naked neck gets a flush of red during courtship, and he belts out an occasional booming call as he gathers several females and takes charge of selecting a nest site. Scraping away a depression in a sandy spot, he begins guarding the location even before the first eggs are laid. In more aggressive territorial encounters with rival males, he commonly uses a rasping hissing sound and a snapping of the beak; a quieter song courts females.

Just Wondering

Ostriches can also produce a belchlike sound. But they can't snore. Dogs, humans and whales snore. Birds and fish don't. How come?

Mating occurs with several females, whose eggs are then laid at the nest site. The male stoops forward, dropping his wings toward a female in quick, quivering movements. Then he eases himself down on the nest. In the days to come, the oldest female will visit the nest repeatedly, each time laying a creamy white egg before him. With his neck and beak he nudges it gently under his body. Younger hens in turn come and deposit an egg, which the male adds to the nest. The normal clutch size is about nineteen eggs, a snug fit beneath a warm, fluffed-up ostrich. Additional eggs roll out in a ring around the nesting site. Without warmth, these eggs are doomed.

Ostrich egg dwarfs a mynah bird egg.

Several days before breaking out, the young chicks can be heard cheeping within the egg. Each hatchling is about the size of a chicken. Like the *kōlea* chick, it is born open-eyed and hardy, ready to leave the nest as soon as its down dries.

Needless to say, ostrich farming failed to catch on in Hawai'i. Soon enough, the fleeting fashion for ostrich feathers passed on. In 1893, many of Trousseau's ostriches died of an unknown stomach disease, and Trousseau himself died in 1894.

Just Wondering

Bird feathers and animal skins have always been hot items as the fads of human fashion come and go: ostrich feather fans and hats, ocelot, jaguar and snow leopard coats, alligator and turtle-skin wallets, bags and shoes. Does respect for other species begin with our not wearing them?

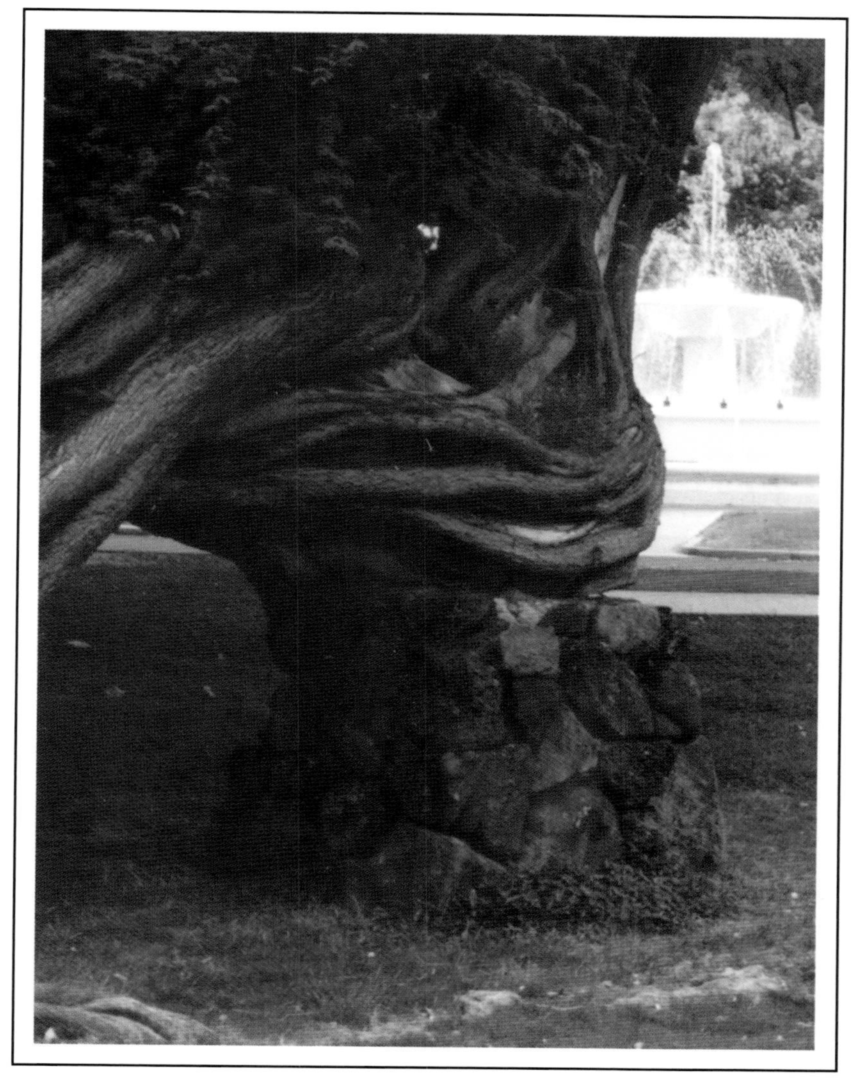

Kapi'olani Park today, with ancient kiawe

Several unsuccessful attempts were made to revive ostrich farming in Waikīkī and later on Kaua'i as well. The remaining birds were shipped back to California in the final year of the century.

Today, you can drive down Trousseau Street in Kapahulu near the Honolulu Zoo and get a glimpse of sturdy *kiawe* trees that still stand in this area. Sometimes festooned with balloons as white as ostrich eggs, these prickly trees now often shelter weekend birthday parties at a place where once, in their sapling days, they provided passing nibbles to Hawai'i's most humongously odd fowl.

Among the animal oddities that were brought to Hawai'i but that failed to establish here were woodpeckers, fireflies, California oysters, chinook salmon, bats, anchovies, the Baya weaverbird, the Guamese swift, and the Montana pronghorn antelope. Today, in theory at least, we are much more restrictive about what is allowed into Hawai'i.

More Ostrich Facts

The ostrich lays the largest egg of all living birds. You'll crack as many as twenty chicken eggs to fill an empty ostrich egg. The huge eggs are said to be very tasty, quite like a hen's egg, but get your egg cooking by 4:30 a.m. to have it hard-boiled for breakfast at 7:00. When refrigerated, the ostrich egg will remain edible up to a year.

Shell thickness generally increases with the size of an egg. The ostrich shell is as thick as a china plate, and yet it allows for enough gas exchange to keep the chick alive for days before hatching. Experiments have shown that it takes about 10 pounds pressing down on a healthy chicken's egg to crush it, 13 pounds on a turkey's, and twice that much to smash a swan's egg. The ostrich egg, which in size and thickness is like a husked coconut, withstands up to about 120 pounds of weight before it cracks and collapses. The largest known egg is that of the extinct flightless elephant bird of Madagascar, a fowl that weighed in at more than 1,000 pounds. Its egg was about 25 pounds and could hold the contents of 9 ostrich eggs, 180 hen eggs, or about 5,000 hummingbird eggs.

Just Wondering

How does the ostrich chick ever break out of its shell?

Faster than any other two-legged animal, ostriches can run at a top speed of about 50 mph in strides of 25 feet, but usually lope along at 30 mph. Their legs are also recognized as powerful weapons, clubbing out bone-crushing kicks with unfailing aim.

Though much of the ostrich's body is featherless—including neck, legs, and portions of the underside—those hairlike feathers it does produce are soft and silky, with a flowing looseness that is much admired by fashion-conscious humans. Ostrich plumes have long been used for decoration and adornment. Kings and queens, popes and sultans have cooled themselves with ostrich-feather fans. African warriors and Greek, Roman and Turkish generals used ostrich plumes in their headdresses. Tutankhamen's chariot was decorated with them and their beautiful, balanced form became a symbol of justice and truth in the hieroglyphs of Egypt. In nineteenth century Hawaiʻi, the *aliʻi* prized the soft ostrich feather as decoration on clothing. Ostrich feathers were also used in *kāhili*, which marked the presence or passage of a person of high rank.

Shiny or sparkly objects often catch the eye of ostriches, blackbirds, crows, mynahs and many other birds. When diamonds were discovered in the gizzard of a South African ostrich—they were probably the rough, dull diamonds that are sometimes found lying on the ground—visions of instant riches trembled in the minds of some settlers there. Hundreds of birds were slaughtered and gutted, but only grinding stones were recovered.

It is not true that ostriches stupidly stick their heads in the sand when faced with a threatening aggressor. They tend to graze slowly with their small heads hung low for long periods. From a distance this creates an impression of headlessness. Just as far from the truth is the notion that the ostrich has a gigantic wishbone capable of making the most marvelous of dreams come true. The ostrich, like other flightless birds, has no wishbone. During flight, a wishbone keeps a bird's ribcage from compressing too far and acts much like a spring, giving the wings something to press against as they flap. The lack of such a wishbone in fossil birds indicates that they were flightless.

»»»»»»»»»»»»»»

The ostrich did not lose the ability to fly because of any defect, but as part of an evolutionary adaptation to life as a grazing bird that retained other effective means—

Remains of extinct flightless goose discovered in ʻŪmiʻi Manu Cave, island of Hawaiʻi

namely hooflike feet and strong leg muscles—to defend itself from predators. In Hawaiʻi, many species of birds as well as numerous insects dispensed with the ability to fly in response to special habitat conditions that safely allowed for the relative advantages of flightlessness. It is believed that seventeen of the sixty or more Hawaiian birds now extinct were flightless. Typically, birds that feed on the ground and are not threatened by predators from which they must escape use their wings very little. As we saw with the *kōlea* in its preparations for a long migration, flying demands a great expenditure of energy, which requires much fuel in the form of food. Dispensing with flight would be an advantage as an energy savings, thus requiring less feeding time.

»»»»»»»»»»»»»»

A mean-spirited but persistent rumor led some early residents of Oʻahu to believe that the spiky *kiawe* was purposely introduced by the missionaries as a nasty but effective way to get Hawaiians to start wearing shoes. The following historic account is surely the more accurate story of this plant's arrival here. The *kiawe* tree was introduced as seed by another Frenchman who arrived in the islands from Paris some seventy years before Trousseau got his idea for an ostrich farm at Kapiʻolani Park. In July, 1827, a priest named Father Alexis Bachelot was sent to Hawaiʻi to establish a Catholic mission. During a final farewell promenade with friends in the King's Garden in Paris, Father Bachelot absentmindedly pocketed a few seeds from a thorny, lacy-leafed tree there. Bachelot took up residence on Fort Street in Honolulu, and eventually planted the seeds, thus introducing what would soon become the most common tree of Hawaiʻi's dryland habitat. Father Bachelot's first *kiawe* was cut down in 1918. A preserved chunk of the tree's trunk can still be seen at the downtown mission church toward the *ma uka* end of what is today called the Fort Street Mall.

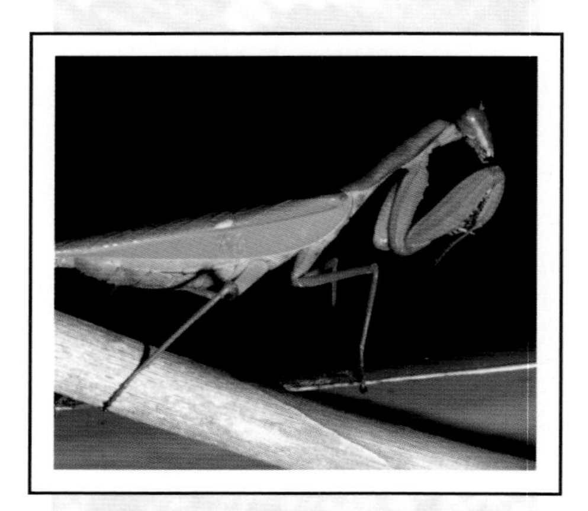

Other English Name: Chinese mantis
Hawaiian Name: *ʻŪhini pule*
Scientific Name: *Tenodera angustipennis*
Area of Origin: Asia
Date of Arrival: 1900

Water hyacinth flower

Orchid in full bloom

Filling Up On Family

The Praying Mantis

Arrival in Hawaiʻi

The goggle-eyed praying mantis was first spotted in the Hāmākua District of the Big Island near the town of Hilo. The year was 1900. An egg capsule probably arrived onboard a ship from Asia, and the young flew or blew off the harbored boat. Adult praying mantises were found in Waikīkī on Oʻahu in 1918 and quickly dispersed to other places around the island to feed on the many insect pests. There are nearly two thousand species of mantises worldwide, six of which now live in Hawaiʻi.

Habitat

Although the praying mantis is seen only infrequently, this has more to do with its coloring and behavior than its actual numbers, for it is now quite a common insect in Hawaiʻi. Lime green to leaf brown, the lean, broad-headed mantis's stick-thin body easily blends with the grasses and bushes of our gardens.

Views

"Over millions of years of evolutionary time, mantids have occupied all accessible regions that have a suitable climate. They abound especially in tropical and subtropical areas and have adapted by protective color and form to a variety of habitats. In a tropical forest, for example, green foliage mantids occupy leafy levels, from shrubs to forest canopy, while brownish, leaf-litter species thrive on and near the forest floor. In a multiplicity of variations, there are flowerlike, twiglike, antlike, lichenlike, barklike mantids—and more."

(E.S. Ross, 1984)

Many species of praying mantises have taken the art of camouflage to a very profitable extreme. Both the Malaysian and African flower mantises look so much like blossoms that insects, finding the "flowers" irresistibly attractive, are lured to them. The insects just as quickly find themselves snapped tight in the mantis's spiked forelegs.

Views

"Flowers are concerned with three things: sex, bribery and advertisement."

(D. Morris, 1990)

Just Wondering

What in the world does Desmond Morris mean?

Food

The praying mantis is nearly undetectable to the human eye as it waits, poised in ambush for its prey, front legs extending upward and forward, appearing to be in prayer. Its intent is much more fearsome, however. Its forelegs are cocked, poised to flash forward at a speed of one-twentieth of a second and snap shut like jackknife blades at the approach of an unsuspecting insect. Sharp spines along the leg impale the prey in an inescapable viselike clamp. The praying mantis has a voracious appetite. It eats all kinds of insects, including bees, wasps and other mantises. Like the bufo, which safely devours centipedes, scorpions and bees, the mantis deftly avoids getting stung.

The mantis is a patient hunter and will wait motionless for long periods. Now and again, its waxy body begins swaying rhythmically from side to side as if in the wind. It is quite an eerie sight to see the weird, trance-like sway of a big mantis and the keen gaze of its alien eyes, which, with uncanny intelligence, stare up at the intruding human. A mantis often begins its sway just before striking. The purpose of the sway may be to mesmerize a prey or perhaps to gauge striking distance.

Actually, despite appearances, mantises are quite harmless to humans. Like their insect relatives the roaches and grasshoppers, they give only the occasional nip with their strong mandible jaws.

Usually a mantis flees when threatened, taking flight with a crispy rustling of its wings. On occasion, however, it rears back in a threatening stance. Turning to confront its adversary, the mantis lifts its wings and raises its folded forelegs to either side of its gaping jaws and glowering eyes. Then it begins a menacing swaying to and fro. This puffed up-posturing is mostly bluff, but many a human has fled in fright at such a formidable encounter.

Just Wondering

The puffed-up pose of the mantis is a common animal signal of threat or alarm, similar to the anole lizard's flexing of its reddish chin flap to frighten other males or the bristling of an angry cat's fur. When you have a fright does your hair stand on end? Do ghost stories give you goose bumps?

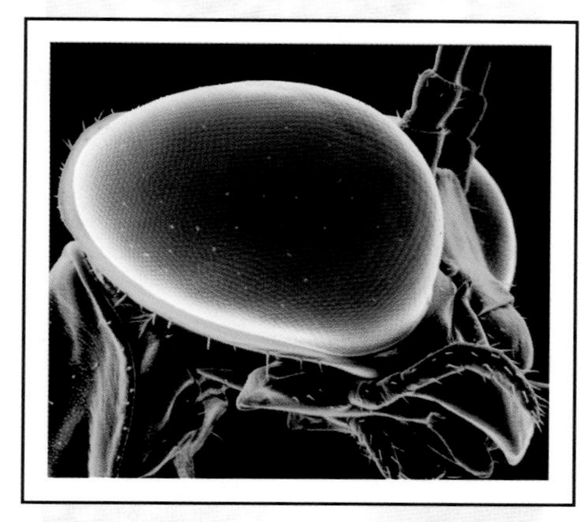

Face to face with a mantis. Lower photo shows magnification x 20

Reproduction

The female mantis is generally larger than the male and a ferocious predator. This makes her a dangerous partner. During mating, the female may abruptly turn on the male, clutch him and begin to eat him head first. Some scientists see this as providing an immediate, protein-rich energy surge that fuels the egg-laying that is soon to take place, similar to the blood-drinking of the female mosquito before she deposits her egg raft.

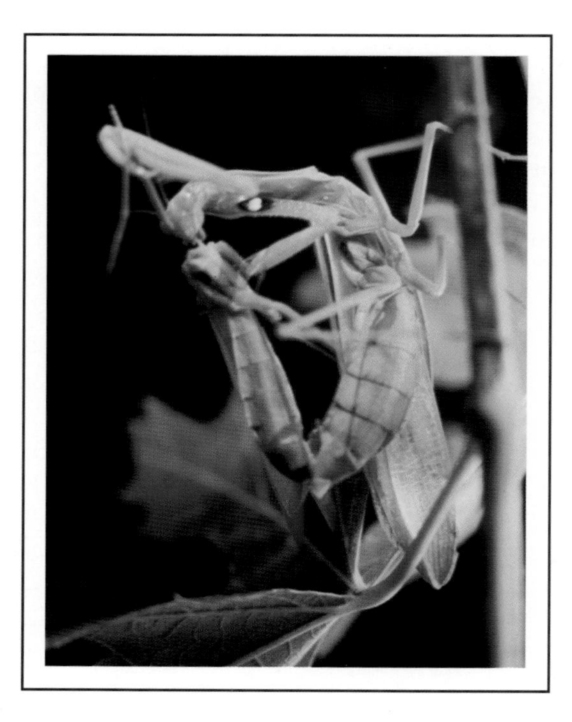

Voracious continental predators imported for gardens: When a male mantis nears a female to mate, she seizes and eats him while his headless body writhes to achieve intromission, fertilizing eggs to be enriched by his own nutrients.

Mantis eggs are housed in a frothy, clumplike egg capsule, which the female, poised head down, spews from the end of her abdomen and glues to a branch, a railing post or the side of a building. The case dries and hardens a glazed brown, providing protection for some two hundred developing offspring within. Porous as pumice, the mantis egg capsule gives good insulation against heat and cold. In temperate climates, cocoons shelter the young through chill winter months and are equally effective in preventing them from drying out during periods of drought. Certain wasps, however, easily drill into the case and parasitize the eggs. In Hawai'i, tiny wasp holes are frequently seen in mantis egg cases.

The young creep out of unparasitized cocoons through slits on the side of the egg case and dangle from a thin thread as their outside skeleton stiffens to hard armor. Wingless, they are otherwise exact replicas of their parents.

The first to appear waits for the next, seizes it and eats it. The third may escape only to turn and consume the fourth, and then itself be devoured by the next. Unless another food source is available, this cannibalistic slaughter continues as the many offspring hatch forth: some survive; most die. Sometimes only half a dozen young are left. Nature offsets the huge losses by ensuring that the female produces many egg cases—up to ten in a laying season.

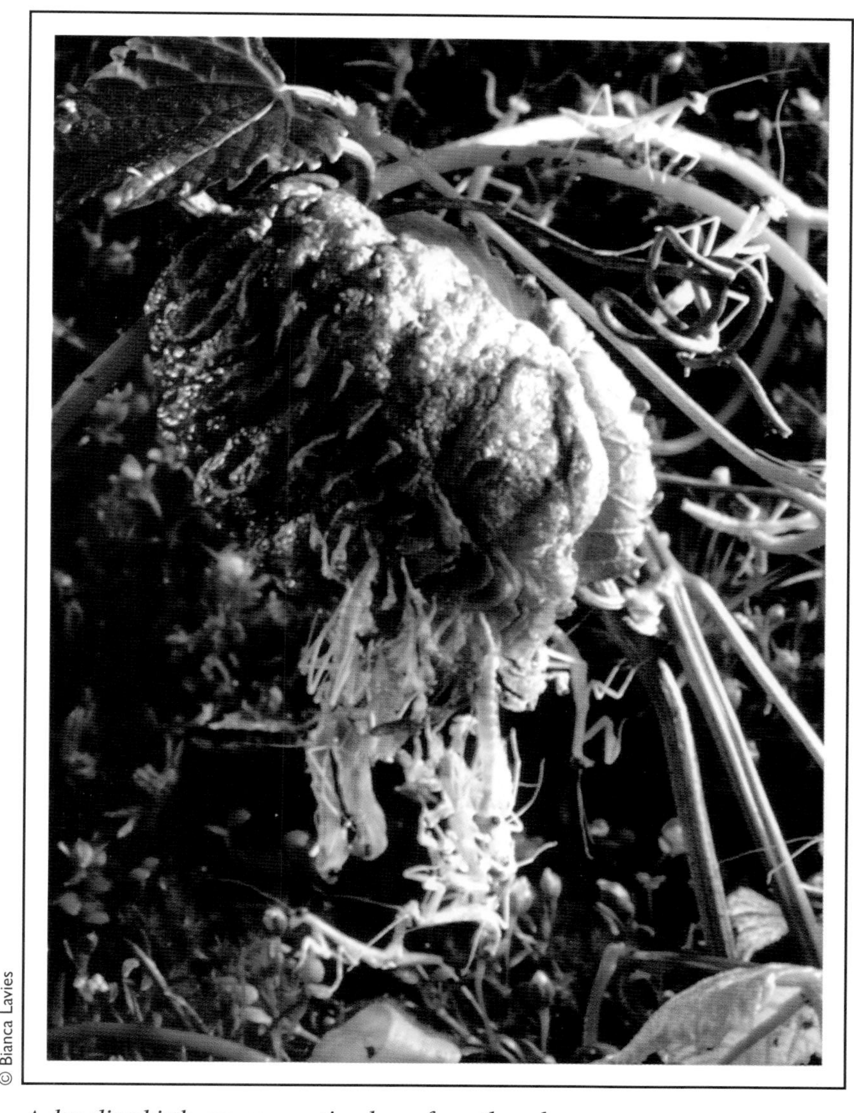

© Bianca Lavies

A dangling birth: young mantises hang from threads.

More Praying Mantis Facts

Like geckos letting go of their tails, mantises occasionally drop one or more of their hind legs to escape danger or capture. This process of self-amputation is called "autotomy," which literally means "self-cutting." The animal is equipped with a special muscle, which it can contract, causing the limb to snap off. Usually a detached leg is replaceable. If a front leg is lost, however, the mantis will be unable to hunt properly and may starve to death. Another defensive trick used by the mantis when threatened is its swaying slowly side to side. Its beige, sticklike body, mimicking a stem moving in the wind, blurs nearly invisibly in a breezy clutter of branches.

Just Wondering

Dropping a leg, claw or tail to make a quick escape is a remarkable ability. Can you imagine leaving an arm behind to finish a math assignment while the rest of you goes surfing? Actually, humans do have abilities in this area that aren't quite so dramatically visible as the thrashing gecko tail on your kitchen floor. Every few days nearly your whole stomach lining is replaced, renewing itself for the tough task of digesting food. All the red blood cells in your body are replaced every 120 days. What other parts of your body are replacing themselves? What seems to be the purpose of these replacements?

The Greeks considered the praying mantis to have supernatural powers. Perhaps the frank and owl-wise expression of its bulgy eyes stirred an uneasy awe in the Greeks: they gave the insect the name "mantis," which was their word for "prophet" and "soothsayer." The eyes of many insects, including the praying mantis, are brown or green. At night, the eye pigment is absorbed by surrounding tissue. More light penetrates, and the eyes turn a beady black.

A long-held belief in rural America warned that if a praying mantis spat in your face you would go permanently blind. The praying mantis doesn't spit. In the American South it was believed that the brownish "tobacco juice" liquid that sometimes seeps from a mantis's mouth could, on contact, kill a mule. Thus mantises were referred to as "mule killers" by some farmers.

In the Orient, praying mantises are kept as pets in little bamboo cages. In days past, images of the praying mantis were often engraved on Japanese sword guards so that the insect's aggressive nature might inspire a *samurai* warrior. The combative posturing of the mantis is also said to be imitated in certain gestures of *kung fu*, the martial art of ancient China.

In many countries mantises—along with grasshoppers, bees and termites—are among the insects commonly eaten by people. In ancient Hawai'i *'ūhini pa'a wela* (grasshoppers) were gathered, strung on stiff grass stems and broiled for food. As herds of cattle and goats ate out their host plant, the edible grasshoppers became extinct.

Just Wondering

In days past, **kōlea, honu** *and dog were relished by the people of this land. In South Africa, the Bantu people eat termites; on the northern tundra, Eskimos eat seal and whale. The French are famous for their cuisine, which includes rabbit and horse meat, frogs and snails. Americans are big on Big Macs and Coke. What determines what we eat? Or what we don't eat?*

When the female mantis devours her mate, or her offspring gobble up their siblings, they are practicing cannibalism, a characteristic not uncommon among many animals. At least 140 known species show cannibalistic behavior, including several animals described in this book. The word "cannibal" was coined by Christopher Columbus in reporting on a human-eating people he encountered on an island named Canibales near what today are Cuba and Haiti. In the animal world there are two types of cannibalism. Active cannibals seek out and kill their own kind, then eat them. Passive cannibals happen upon the dead body of one of their own species and feed on it. Scientists suspect the female mantis gains a quick protein boost from eating her mate just before laying her eggs. Cannibalism can also result from conditions of environmental stress, such as overpopulation or food scarcity. A species' chances of survival increase when some members succeed into adulthood by feeding on their siblings. Crows are known to devour the eggs and chicks of rival pairs. This perhaps improves their own access to a limited food source and thereby ensures the successful rearing of their young. But among many species, cannibalism is just one of the common dangers of being alive and seems to have little to do with environmental stress in nature.

Just Wondering

When Robinson Crusoe discovered human prints in the sand of his shipwreck island, the horror of human cannibalism shivered through him—and on to the reader as well. The thought of eating human flesh is overwhelmingly repulsive to us. For a long period of human history, however, and in a variety of cultures, the taboos in this area were less rigid than they are today. Again, what determines what or who we eat?

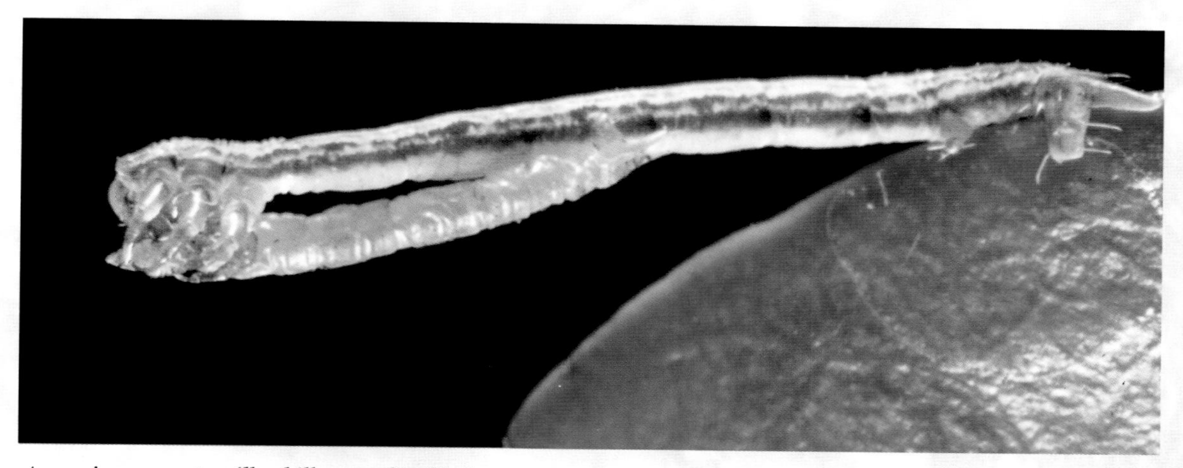

A carnivorous caterpillar kills one of its kind.

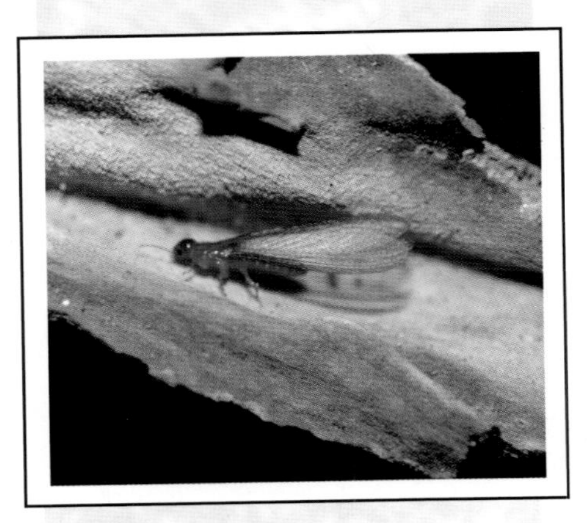

Other English Name:
Formosan subterranean termite
Hawaiian Name: *Naonao lele*
Scientific Name:
Coptotermes formosanas
Area of Origin: Asia
Date of Arrival: 1913

Typical wooden house in Honolulu, circa 1900

Streetcar, circa 1913

Quivering Wings and Stained Glass

The Ground Termite

Arrival in Hawaiʻi

Ground termites were first found in Honolulu in 1913. Most likely, a steamship from Asia carried a nest in the dark dirt ballast of its dank hull or in a chunk of infested wood. Such ballast was commonly used to stabilize a ship carrying light cargo. Later, when the ship was booked for outgoing freight, the ballast was shoveled onshore, letting loose on land any stowaway creatures concealed in the dirt or rocks.

The swarming of the termites, most thickly in May, probably coincided with the ship's berthing in Honolulu harbor. We can imagine a quiet early evening in port. Probably nobody noticed the first small flitting blur of termites seeping up from a ship's hold or slipping off an onshore ballast heap, reddish quivering wings lifting in a tangle out over the glimmering harbor water, then drawing inland to dim downtown street lamps.

It was a small but ominous first swarming. An abundance of food awaited in the many wooden buildings that made up Honolulu town in those days and the sturdy lamp poles that gave the city steady light by night and stop points for streetcars by day.

Those streetcars would provide a convenient distribution network for the newly introduced termites, extending them in a rapid spread across town. Mule-drawn carts used in the early days had, by 1913, been replaced by "modern streetcar equipment" with comfortable open cars operated by a conductor and a motorman. Regular evening service was even assured to the country points of Kalihi and Waikīkī. As termites swarmed in brown clouds at downtown lamp lights, open streetcars pulled to a stop below, took on passengers and flitting insects alike, and carried them out along the line to the farthest points of the district of Honolulu.

Food

The streetlamp poles also became convenient food sources for the millions of "flying ants," as Hawaiians called them. Previously, poles made of untreated timber had lasted up to fifteen years. Ground termites were now chewing through them within six months.

Living in darkness, termites gnaw wood and thus satisfy their voracious appetites for cellulose, a starch that is the main structural component in the cell walls of plants. Cellulose cannot be digested, however, without the help of tiny protozoa that live in the termite gut. Termites are not born with these little helpers. After hatching, the young termites are fed predigested cellulose, which contains the one-celled creatures, from the mouths of adults. The protozoa in turn benefit from the protected habitat provided by the termite gut. This type of relationship that is helpful to both partners is called symbiosis. There are many examples of such cooperation in nature.

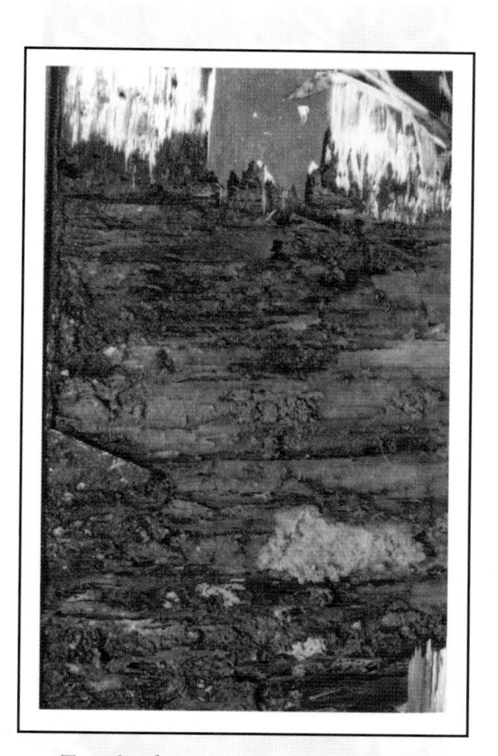

Termite damage

Just Wondering

"How can [dry-wood] termites live on dry wood and yet have soft bodies full of juices?"

(F.L. Behnke, 1977)

Habitat

Ground termites, sheltered in the moist earth, create great and sometimes quite expansive nests. They leave the nest only through an elaborate and often far-reaching system of protective tunnels. These passageways are made of a brown, papier mâché–like material that workers produce in their mouths using dirt, saliva, and their own excrement. With the help of these sheltering galleries and a keen sense of smell, termites cross woodless areas and find cellulose. The passageways' construction preserves moisture and humidity within the nest so the eggs do not dry out.

Papier mâché-like nesting material

Reproduction

The nest itself is a chamberlike cavity hollowed out of the soil from which the tube galleries lead off to feeding grounds. At the center of the nest lies the colossally swollen queen, an amazingly prolific egg layer believed to be the world's longest-lived insect. Known to lay eggs for up to fifty years, some queen termites may live a full century. A single queen was once monitored as she laid over fifty thousand eggs in one day. As an egg machine, the queen grows so obese that she must be fed and even moved by the pale, blind workers that serve her.

Most insects, when eggs are laid, take no further interest in their offspring. Not so the social insects—the bees, wasps, termites, and ants—who have an elaborate system for caring for their young.

In Hawai'i, we grow accustomed to termites' whirling at dusk on warm, windless evenings in summer. May is the month of greatest swarming for ground termites in Hawai'i. They spew out of their nests through tiny holes made in the tunnels. Wingless, blind and big-headed soldier termites also spill out and take up guard positions, protecting the nest from predators. Within half an hour the winged termites have all left. The soldiers return to the nest, and the tiny exit holes are plugged by worker termites.

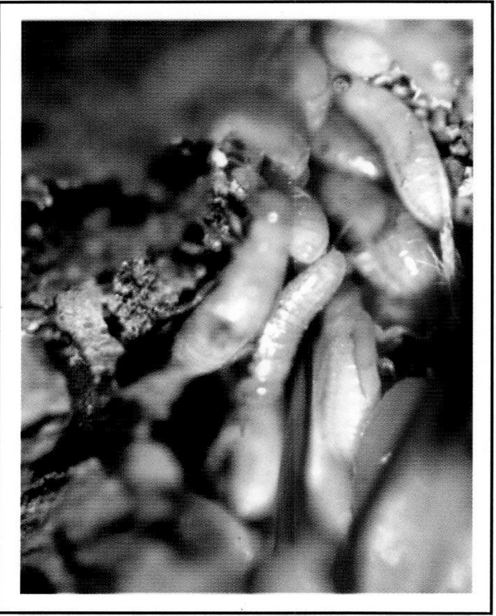

Termite larvae, disturbed by sudden daylight, huddle tightly.

Views

"A swarm or colonizing flight is a multiplication process, one of the ways nature provides for scattering the species and dispersing colonies into new habitats. The chance of a single male and female establishing a new colony would be one in thousands. Swarms vary in size, but a large one is more likely to be successful since not all the termites will be intercepted by predators. A swarming is subject to the law of probabilities."

(F.L. Behnke, 1977)

Just Wondering

A subterranean termite nest may contain a million or more offspring, many of which will eventually leave on one of the periodic swarming outflights that establish new nests elsewhere. This process of swarming holds many mysteries that are only partly understood by scientists. What, for example, are the conditions that trigger the precisely timed swarming instinct in the nest? Chemical secretions from the queen? Behavioral signals from a population of worker termites whose numbers are growing too cramped? Atmospheric conditions such as temperature or humidity level?

Nothing, it seems, shields our homes from these destructive intruders that chew even the stoutest two-by-four timber to a tidy heap of pinhead-size droppings. The culprits might well be another species living in Hawai'i, called dry-wood termites, but several characteristics of reproduction are found among termites everywhere. If we look carefully we will see typical behavioral patterns in those that enter our houses.

Wings are quickly discarded, broken off along a fracture line on the back side. The termite simply bends its wings backward against the ground and off they snap. The female then lifts her abdomen and holds it stiff and still. A scent gland underneath sprays a fragrance that attracts males to her. Paired off, the female and male begin a curious chase, the male speeding along behind the scurrying female, now and then prodding her with his antennae as they rush on. They are searching for a nesting site. On occasion several persistent males will line up behind a lone female like boxcars behind a tiny racing locomotive. This tandem chasing can last as long as several hours. Finally, the two termites end their frantic rushing and groom each other quietly. Mating takes place after the choice of residence is made. Then they begin to build their first small nesting chamber.

The male termite remains an active partner in establishing a new colony. He may stay with the queen for many years to come. For the other social insects, mating usually marks the end of the male's role in assuring a new generation of offspring.

In a couple of weeks the queen lays a small number of eggs. It will take time before the new nest builds sufficient strength of numbers to enable her to lay the many thousands of eggs daily of which she is capable. For twenty-one days there is much tending of the eggs, with continuous licking that keeps them clean and prevents mold from growing. When the first young hatch, the male assumes the greater share of responsibility, feeding and grooming until the colony is established.

In time there evolves a highly complex community based on a caste system of wingless workers, soldiers armed with fierce pincer-jaws, and winged termites that soon swirl out in summer swarms and whose task is to establish new colonies.

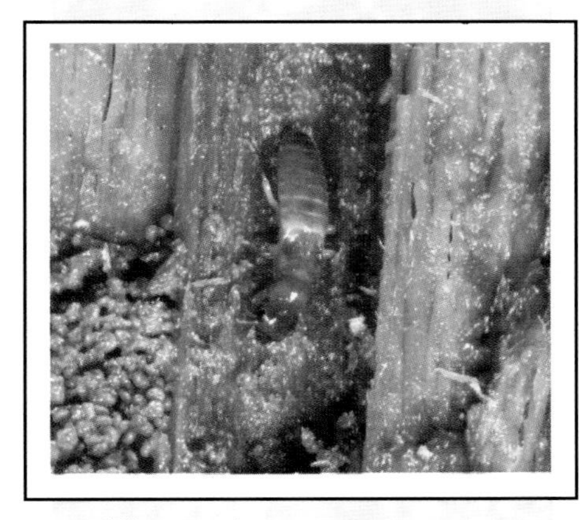

Soldier termite

Just Wondering

Termites spend most of their lives in blind darkness. Why then do they rush to streetlights and house lights in their brief moment of flight? If we flicked off our many lights, would these critters all flutter off to the full moon and leave us well alone?

Pure white larva scurries along a pitch black tunnel.

More Termite Facts

In many parts of the world termites are eaten as a delicacy. They are said to have a sweet, pineapple-like flavor. When cooked, they throw off a rich oil that gives a buttery flavor to fried chicken. As a source of protein, termites rank high: the percentage of protein in beef is 17.4; in chicken, between 20.6 and 23.4; in cooked termites, as high as 45.6. The Bantu tribe of South Africa gathers swarming termites as they spew from the nest opening into a pail of water. They pull off the wings and roast the termites on an oil-smeared hot stone or pan until almost crisp. Adding a sprinkle of salt to taste, they munch them like toasted sunflower seeds.

House tented for dry-wood termites

Just Wondering

Termite Burgers! A food for the future?

Just Wondering

Humans go about the world behaving as if they own the place: spraying insecticide on bugs they don't like, causing the extinction of plants and animals at a rate of one species an hour, polluting waters, tearing down rain forests, cloning animals. Is there anything in nature to suggest that it cares more for our human species than for termites?

Of the millions of termites that flit about our homes, only a tiny fraction survive and start nests of their own. Bufos, geckos and bulbuls are but a few of the many predators that eagerly stuff themselves on termites. Enough termites do survive, however, to cost homeowners in Hawai'i considerable sums of money yearly. Termite-related damage in the islands caused by ground and dry-wood termites amounts to well over $150 million annually. There are about two thousand species of termites worldwide, four of which have been introduced to Hawai'i. Of the others, many very destructive species are common in places that send tourists and cargo to our islands every year. The arrival of more species to Hawai'i poses a very real threat.

The first ground termites ever reported on Maui were discovered in April, 1963. The nest was located in a house on High Street in Wailuku, across from Wailuku Elementary School.

Thousands of soldier termites with biting jaws protect the nest and each other from their many enemies. Different termite species are equipped with biological defense gadgets of their own: some worker termites act as mimics; concealed beneath dried leaves, they may make a sound like a snake's hiss that scares away predators. Some termite workers defend the colony against enemies by literally

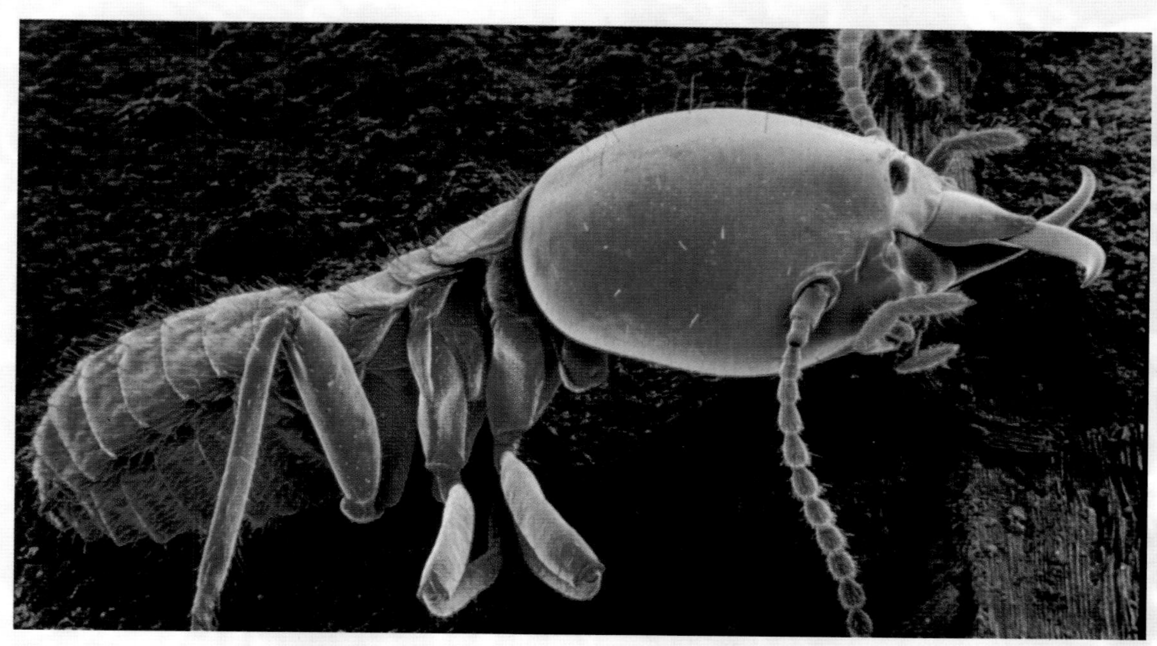

Soldier termite, magnified 11 times

blowing themselves to pieces and spewing their attackers with a turpentine-like slime from their insides.

⋙⋙⋙⋙

Though they may not count among humanity's closest animal friends, termites have a precious role to play. In forests, termites speed the return of nutrients to the earth by recycling dead trees and wood debris, hastening the creation of the new soil that is always forming on the forest floor.

⋙⋙⋙⋙

Like a prehistoric insect trapped forever in a piece of glowing amber, a single winged termite image is fixed in a stained-glass window at St. Andrew's Cathedral in Honolulu. In the 1950s, ravenous termites destroyed the cathedral roof. A decision was made to add a beautiful window as part of the renovation work. To honor the little critters that had created the opportunity, a brownish termite image was crafted into the glass. This serves as a reminder that the little recycling termite, which appears so destructive in the eyes of man, may, in the greater picture of creation, provide an important function that actually benefits humanity!

Stained glass window, St. Andrew's Cathedral, Honolulu (detail)

⋙⋙ ***Just Wondering*** ⋙⋙

How about friend roach?

Torn Tarp, Skim Milk

The Brush-Tailed Rock Wallaby

Hawaiian Name:
Kanakalū Kalihi
Scientific Name:
Petrogale penicilliata
Area of Origin: Australia
Date of Arrival: 1916

Arrival in Hawai'i

In 1916, a ship whose homeport was in Australia put in at Honolulu Harbor with an assortment of circus animals onboard. They were unusual animals, and they were for sale. Among them were several miniature kangaroos called brush-tailed rock wallabies.

Richard H. Trent, who lived on the sparsely populated slope of 'Ālewa Heights, was interested. He collected animals as a hobby and, moreover, he thought that a pair of marsupials might attract buyers to his subdivision. 'Ālewa Heights is the hillside running up the west shoulder of Nu'uanu Valley. Although it overlooks Honolulu Harbor and the city center, in the early part of this century the location was considered remote.

Mr. Trent paid $100 each for a pair of the wallabies. The female carried a joey. Returning home late that night, Mr. Trent decided to house his new pets in a temporary shelter in his yard. Their strong odor attracted a pack of wild dogs. They tore at the tarp wall of the pen and attacked the wallabies, scaring them off *ma uka*. The joey was flung from its mother's pouch and mauled to death by the dogs, but both parents escaped into the dark.

Wallaby country: a Kalihi hillside

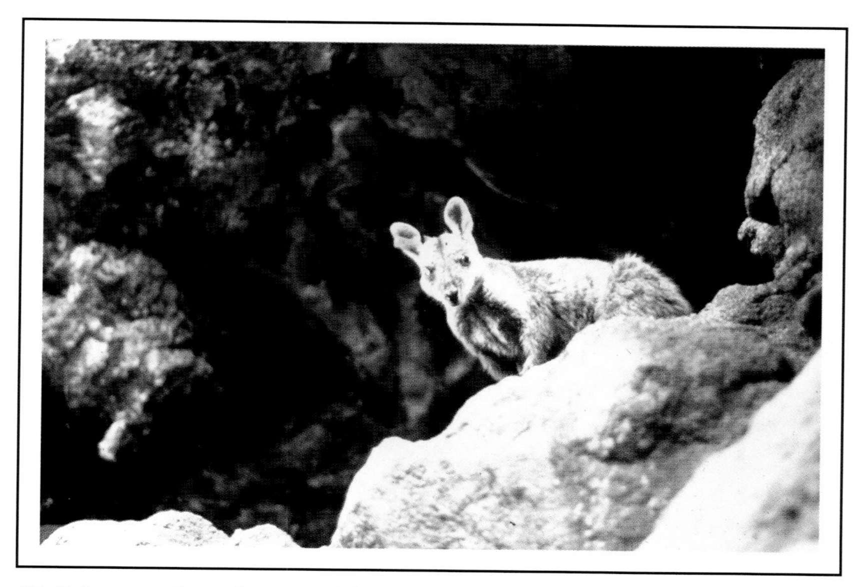

Wallaby peers down from a Kalihi ridge.

Mr. Trent's offer of a $25 reward for their recovery went unclaimed. Eventually the wallabies made their way across Kapālama Heights, now the site of the Kamehameha Schools, and down into Kalihi to a slim, rugged ridge about halfway up the valley. Their descendants remain there to this day, some 100 to 150 living on the craggy ridges of upper Kalihi Valley. The population seems stable: an occasional wallaby is killed by a dog, hit by a car on Likelike Highway, or shot as target practice by a thoughtless gun owner.

The little kangaroo-like animals Trent purchased are indeed quite a curiosity. Wallabies have long snouts, long ears and stout tails, which are used for bracing and balancing as they clamber over the rocky ridges where they live. While their bodies may appear cumbersome, sure-footed wallabies can get across craggy outcroppings of rock with the nimble agility and grace of a goat. Thickly padded hind feet allow them to skip from rock to rock without a slip, pausing from time to time as they bask in the early sun or nibble at the grass or leaves that make up their diet. On level ground, however, a wallaby wobble is awkward and slow. Occasionally a wallaby will grunt, but its normal sound is more of a hiss. If danger threatens, it thumps the ground with its hind paws. Wallabies are primarily nocturnal feeders, but are sometimes seen in the first soft sun as morning moves from the light of dawn to the bright of day.

Habitat

The original Australian habitat of the brush-tailed rock wallaby has a temperate climate, but the Hawaiian wallabies have adapted surprisingly well to the tropical heat of their adopted land. Shaggy pelts that evolved in the chill of the ancestral habitat have,

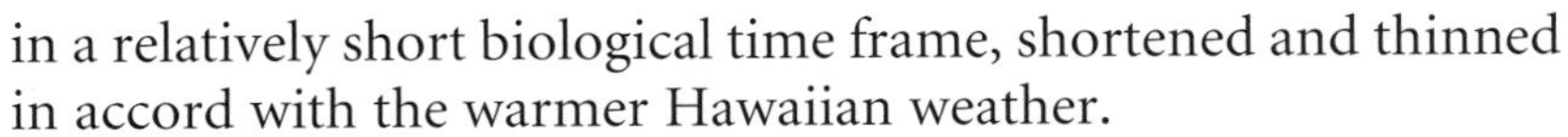

in a relatively short biological time frame, shortened and thinned in accord with the warmer Hawaiian weather.

Wallabies are exceedingly agile at climbing the steepest rocks, thanks to their large, padded hindfeet equipped with sharp claws and flexible middle toes. The pads on their feet are like sandpaper. In Australia, their treading about has smoothed the stone floors of the caves they inhabit to a marble shine.

Reproduction

Wallabies are mammals, but unlike the other mammals discussed in this book—the *poi* dog and the pig—they are marsupials. "Marsupial" means "pouch bearing" and refers to the pouch in which they carry their young. Actually, it is no more than a deep fold of skin on the underside of the female's body. This is the marsupial womb, cradle and comfort chamber. These creatures are throwbacks to an ancient time when mammals first appeared on Earth, a time when dinosaurs and reptiles ruled the world. With the eventual disappearance of dinosaurs, mammals got the upper evolutionary hand and became much more plentiful and varied. Many species evolved a placenta in place of the marsupial pouch. Today, while marsupials are found in North and South America, Australia is the land that comes to mind when we think of marsupials.

The wallaby egg is fertilized inside the female, where it begins development. The premature fetus—blind, bare and barely larger than a honeybee—somehow grapples and muddles its way through the dense forest of fur up its mother's belly, where it enters her pouch. While its eyes and ears are sealed shut, its nostrils are wide open, and it smells its way along the six-inch path to the pouch.

Wallaby joey gets its first physical.

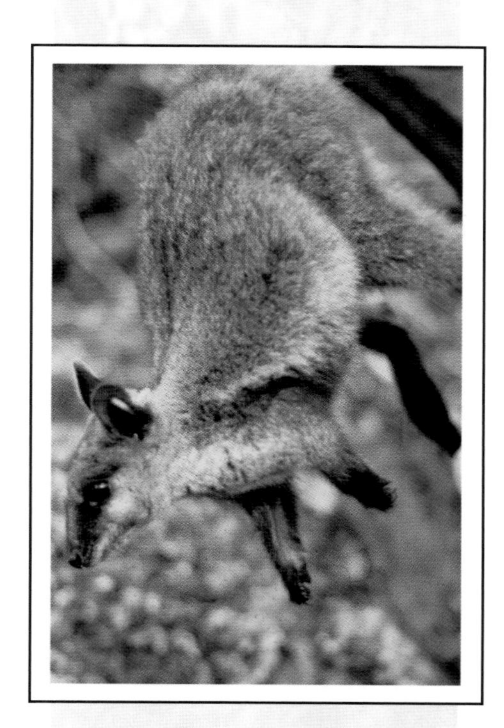

There it clamps to a small teat that quickly swells, locking the baby to its mother for the next several months. Once the baby latches on, it is nearly impossible to detach it from the teat without tearing its mouth. The undeveloped marsupial, which at this moment weighs about one-thirtieth of an ounce and measures three-fourths of an inch, is unable to suck. By contracting muscles in her mammary glands the mother presses milk down her offspring's throat. A female marsupial often develops a spare embryo, which is held in reserve next to the developing joey for several months. If all goes well with the older sibling, the additional embryo either disintegrates or continues to develop.

The growth of the embryo can be "put on hold" during periods of drought. When the life-giving rain returns, the embryo resumes its development. If the wallaby pouch contains offspring of different ages and different stages, the female can produce milk that is individually formulated. The fetus is fed a low-fat formula, while its older sibling gets a richer mixture.

A joey stays put in the pouch up to a year, until fully developed and able to venture out, quickly tumbling back in fear or fatigue.

This little marsupial serves as a good representative of the many, many plants and animals introduced to Hawai'i at the personal whim of a single person. Unlike the mild little wallaby, however, most of these private introductions have had negative effects on the land. The voracious, fruit-eating bulbul, for example, is rumored to have been imported in the mid-1960s by a Makiki matron who thought it a cute cage bird. When a storm overturned the outdoor cage, several bulbuls escaped into the neighborhood and their offspring have since spread islandwide, causing much damage to fruit and orchid crops.

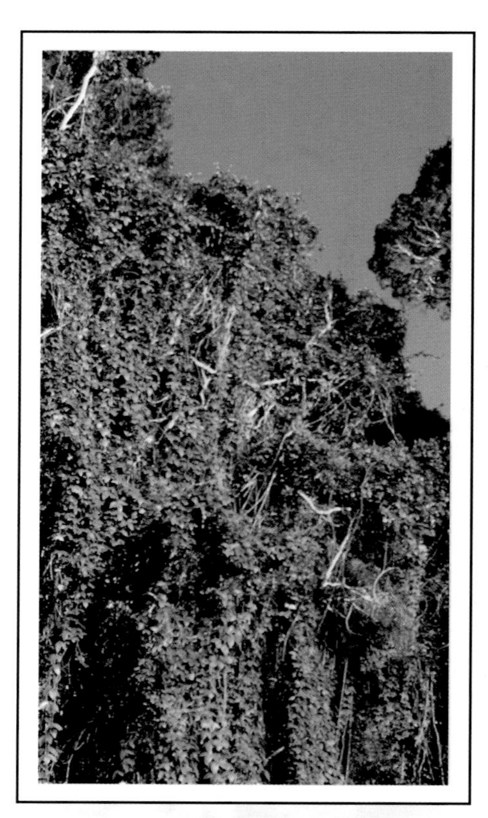

Banana poka suffocates native species

A similar example of a whimsical introduction is that of the banana poka vine, which in all likelihood was first brought to Hawai'i in the 1920s. Its pretty flowers were thought the perfect cover to hide an outhouse at a cattle ranch on the Big Island. The vine has since spread and is a nasty pest in a large area of Hawaiian rain forest.

Many new plants and an assortment of critters still sneak their way to the islands each year in the pockets and briefcases, bags and cartons of arriving passengers. The penalty for smuggling in exotic species is stiff: $25,000 and a year in jail. An amnesty bin located near the airport baggage claim area is the last-chance place to hand over illegal sneak-ins.

Unfortunately, voluntary declaration forms handed out on incoming flights are not taken seriously, and the state's financial and personnel resources for enforcing laws against illegal importations are severely limited. The system is overwhelmed: in 1995, only 133 state and federal inspectors and their 10 sniffing dogs were expected to check on over 25,000 flights carrying 6 million tons of cargo and over 8 million visitors and returning residents into the islands. These figures do not include arrivals by ship or by air mail. The danger to Hawai'i is truly great:

Views

"The silent invasion of Hawai'i by insects, disease organisms, snakes, weeds, and other pests is the single greatest threat to Hawai'i's economy and natural environment and to the health and lifestyle of Hawai'i's people. Pests already cause millions of dollars in crop losses, the extinction of native species, the destruction of native forests, and the spread of disease. But many more harmful pests now threaten to invade Hawai'i and wreak further damage. Even one new pest—like the brown tree snake—could forever change the character of our islands. Stopping the influx of new pests and containing their spread is essential to Hawai'i's future well-being."

(The Coordinating Group on Alien Pest Species, 1999)

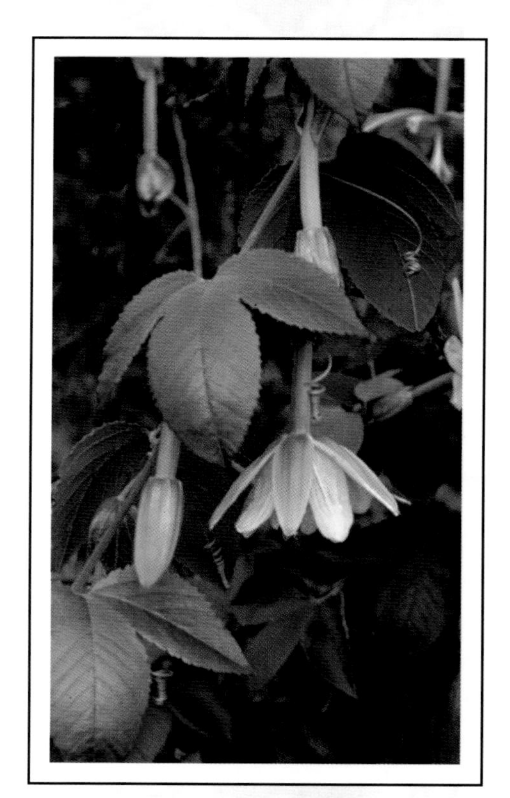

Banana poka: a beauty and a beast

Just Wondering

Nearly twenty thousand packages come by air to Hawai'i every day. Legal restrictions prevent officials from adequately inspecting First Class mail, allowing many pests to enter Hawai'i by way of the mail-order trade. Illegal species such as venomous spiders, a variety of reptiles, giant scorpions, and piranhas are easily sent to island homes. When the privacy rights of the individual interfere with the urgent need for environmental protection, something has got to give. What?

More Wallaby Facts

The color of Kalihi wallabies is more varied than that of their Australian cousins and goes from gray to brown to reddish brown and black with bolder patterning. Wallabies are smaller and paler than their Australian cousins and have larger ears. There are differences as well in skull shape, blood proteins, and enzymes. Indeed, the Hawaiian wallabies seem to be different from any now living in Australia. The original population in Australia may have become extinct, or the Hawaiian population may have evolved dramatically after only eighty generations. In Australia wallabies are adapted to a variety of habitats: one population even lives among surf-splashed boulders on the shore of an island. The Hawaiian wallabies, isolated by thousands of miles from their Australian ancestors, may illustrate that evolution occurs in small steps over a relatively short period of time.

Rapid evolution is one characteristic of life on oceanic islands. Another characteristic is the occurence of small populations and the exceptional occurrence of unique forms. Island ecosystems are by definition fragile. Rapid evolution may be partly due to pressures of the new environment, but it is more likely made possible by what biologists call the "founder effect." Founding a new population with only two individuals means that the genetic variation all subsequent generations have to work with is very limited, and traits can rapidly careen off in one direction or another. For example, if Trent's two wallabies had larger-than-average–sized ears, their descendants may have tended to have large ears, and with no small-eared wallabies to interbreed with, ears may have become larger down through the generations. The founder effect probably played a role in the evolution of many of the small populations of organisms that blew, drifted or flew to the Hawaiian Islands.

Just Wondering

With successive brother-sister matings over a period of years, the wallabies may end up genetically identical. What does this mean for a species?

For many years, observers thought that the wallaby mother licked a path through her thick fur that would guide her young to the teat. It is now thought that her licking is a cleaning reflex that follows the three-minute passage of her young.

The Virginia opossum is one of several American marsupials. The female produces a lot of babies with each batch: as many as twenty-five or thirty blind, pinkish young are born. They rush their way through their mother's fur and into her pouch. Waiting there are thirteen nipples. The first opossums to latch on will live. The laggards will die.

Just Wondering

Half of the opossum babies are wasted because they lose their first race. Only one of a thousand scampering turtle hatchlings reaches adulthood. Crabs, birds, sharks, and barracudas get the others. Does it all come down to dashing and rushing, eating or being eaten? Is nature basically heartless and unfair?

The timid and reclusive wallaby is one of very few exotic introductions to Hawaiʻi that seems to have caused no or only minimal changes to native plants and animals. Its shy nibblings at Kalihi grass and twigs leave little trace. Another grass nibbler, however, has had more harmful effects on the leeward island of Laysan:

Views

"The first men on Laysan in the nineteenth and early twentieth centuries were sealers, guano diggers, feather collectors—all takers. And then, with the idea of contributing, a man from Honolulu introduced rabbits. What he contributed was devastation. Within twenty years the rabbits ate virtually everything green on Laysan all the way down to the nubs, . . . just four of the twenty-five plant species surviving in small numbers and several bird species pushed to extinction by having their habitat gnawed out from under them.

A scientific expedition came in 1923 to get rid of the rabbits. One day the shooters spotted three birds, Laysan honey creepers. The next day a sand storm blew up, gale force, and stung and buffeted all three birds to death—the last of their kind on earth, the only songbirds in the documented history of the world to go extinct within sight and sound of humankind, with the time of the end recorded to the hour."

(Gavan Daws, 1988)

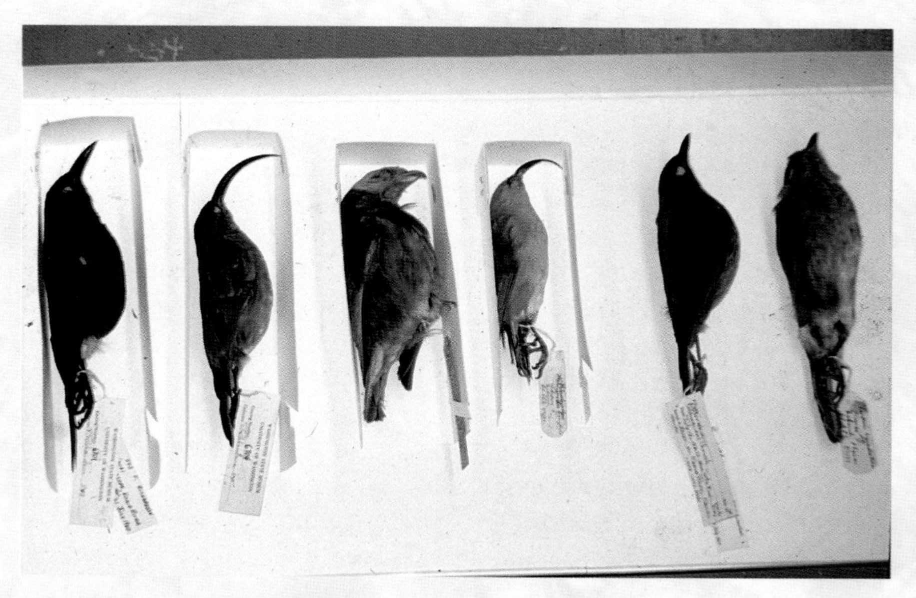

These birds in paper caskets at the Bishop Museum are thought to have become extinct in recent years.

Piggybacking Tadpoles

The Poison Dart Frog

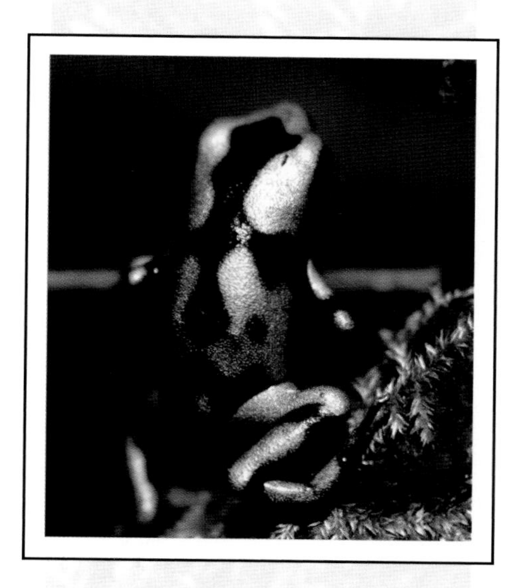

Hawaiian Name: *Poloka Panamā*
Other Name: Gold and Black Poison Frog
Scientific Name: *Dendrobates auratus*
Area of Origin: Central America
Date of Arrival: 1932

Arrival in Hawai'i

Nestling in moist leaves and mossy rocks deep in Mānoa Valley on O'ahu lives a remarkable little frog unlike any other in Hawai'i. Its very name—the poison dart frog—hints at a fascinating creature. In 1932, 206 of these secretive, colorful little frogs were brought to Hawai'i from the islands of Tobogilla in the Gulf of Panama.

Food

The tiny, wide-eyed amphibians—about as big as a *kukui* nut—were shipped here to kill mosquitoes. They feed on all kinds of insects, and are particularly effective in zapping slow-flying mosquitoes near standing water.

Habitat

Released in the back of Mānoa, they have remained there to this day, nearly forgotten near the stream banks and under houses in the adjoining neighborhoods. They have spread as well over the *pali* into the windward valley of Waiāhole, but have not been seen in the adjoining valleys of Makiki or Pālolo. The little frogs forage in leaf litter on the forest floor and sometimes climb into low shrubs. A good time to observe them is after a soaking rain or as morning mist smudges up the view of the valley.

The Mānoa frog is as black as new lava and patterned with rounded markings of a *kukui*-leaf green. This is good coloration on the forest floor, yet—as with the brightly patterned monarch butterfly—advertises a dangerous presence of poison.

Hunters of the Chocó tribe who stalk jaguar, deer, monkeys and birds in the thick forests of Tobogilla have developed a clever way to detect the concealed frogs and make use of their highly toxic poison in the hunt. According to two scientists who observed them collecting frogs, the Chocós imitate the "fiu-fiu, fiu-fiu" peep of the frogs by whistling shrilly while thumping their fingertips lightly on their cheeks. A frog, crouching close by, answers the call, revealing its hiding place. Then, carefully placing a protective leaf against the palms of their hands, the Chocós lift the frogs into a carrying pouch for the trip home.

Back in the village, the hunter skewers the frogs through their mouths along split bamboo sticks called *siuru kika* and toasts them like marshmallows over red coals. Roasting blisters the

frog's skin, causing a sappy ooze to bubble up in droplets along the back. As the milky substance cools, tips of arrows are smeared in it, then set aside to dry in the shade.

The poison from one small frog coats fifty arrow points with a deadly dose, each sufficient to paralyze a deer or a large monkey within seconds. Death follows a short time later. The poison, called *kokoi* by the Chocós, affects both the muscles and nerve system. Oddly, it does not cause any reaction on unbroken human skin, or when taken orally, but is excruciatingly painful when applied to a scratch or tiny cut. Its effectiveness as a killer coating dried on dart tips lasts up to a year.

Just Wondering

Native hunters in Panama use this deadly poison to kill their prey. Then they eat the animal, but they suffer no ill effects. How come?

Reproduction

Frogs are amphibians. "Amphibian" means "double life" and describes a creature that begins life in water but spends most of its adult life on land. The reproductive behavior of the poison dart frog stretches this definition a bit and is just as extraordinary as its powerful poison defense. Most frogs and toads take no role in the care of their offspring from egg stage on, but the poison dart frog is an exception.

Life on a leaf: tadpole and young poison dart frog

These frogs often begin life on a leaf. Following an elaborate courtship, the female deposits a gluey clutch of eggs on a wet leaf or on damp earth that has been carefully cleaned. The male then takes up guard over the eggs. Depending on the weather, it can be a lengthy watch—sometimes lasting as long as two weeks.

When the tadpoles hatch, they wriggle up onto the back of the male and are attached by a sticky substance produced by mucous glands. For several hours newborn offspring backpack safely along as father frog treks off in search of a suitable pool of water. On the forest floor of Mānoa, these beautiful frogs frequently place their young in broken bottles or other human garbage where water collects.

Just Wondering

The male's role as transporter of offspring is not so unusual. In over half of all fish species known to care for their young, it is the male who assumes the responsibility. A remarkable example is that of the sea horse. It is the male that gets pregnant when the female presses her eggs into his protective, womblike pouch, where they are then fertilized. Later, he will experience contractions and give birth by spurting them out. Are male and female roles in species not as firm and fixed as most of us are led to believe?

The male carefully delivers each tadpole to a pool of water and, having ended his parenting chores, hops off. Soon the tadpole changes to a froglet, a little copy of its parents: the magical circle of life continues. Indeed, each time a tiny, shiny, water-bound tadpole sprouts legs, slithers to shore, and begins to breathe air, it reenacts the ancient shift from sea to land that made life in the open air possible:

Views

"[T]he first amphibians left the waters and came ashore, exchanging one element for another. They performed the slow miracle of ceasing to take oxygen from the water and acquired the means of absorbing it from the air. From the first amphibians evolved the reptiles, the birds and the mammals, including ourselves. . . . The miracle—rather speeded up—of switching from gills to lungs is still performed today by the 2,600 species of frogs and toads and their near relatives during the development from tadpole to adult."

(D. Stivens, 1974)

Just Wondering

The human embryo at a very early stage still has gill slits. Are we more like the toad than we'd care to admit?

There are fewer and fewer poison dart frogs in Mānoa Valley these days. It is not known if this is part of the worrisome world-wide decline in the numbers of amphibians. It is a fact, however, that several O'ahu collectors are exporting these intriguing little frogs for thirty-five dollars apiece to mainland pet shops.

Just Wondering

What selective pressures may have caused ancestral fish to move to a part-aquatic, part-terrestrial lifestyle to become amphibians?

More Frog and Toad Facts

Hawaiian warriors of old smeared their own spear tips with a highly toxic poison. This was not made from the mucous secretions of poison dart frogs, however, for there were none in Hawai'i before 1932. The source of their killer poison was *ka limu make o* Hāna, "the deadly seaweed of Hāna." A Hawaiian scholar writing in the 1800s warned: "This was the fastest-working poison, like the deadliest *haole* poison, and perhaps more potent." The reddish *limu* was found in tidepools near Hāna, Maui. Today, cancer researchers are investigating this seaweed and the soft coral it lives with in hopes of developing beneficial medicines. The poison, called palytoxin, is found in the soft coral of certain tidepools. This substance is so powerful that just one molecule is sufficient to cause the death of a cell.

A frog or toad tongue may be nearly as long as its body. With lightning speed and sticky tip, it is a deadly tool for zapping passing insects that enter an area around their bodies known as "the snapping zone." The tongue is rooted close to the front of the mouth, a position that extends its striking range. It is so elastic that it can stretch to about twice its resting length. Toads and frogs are highly sensitive to any movement and react with a quick flick of their tongue to the slightest insect motion. Their eyes are such sensitive motion-detectors that when humans designed the electronic eye they used the frog eye as a model. Unlike cats and geckos, frogs and toads do not react with a strike at only a scurrying prey. Bufos have been found feeding sluggishly on a bowl of leftover cat pellets.

Not all species referred to as poison-dart frogs are strongly toxic. Of 135 identified species of *Dendrobates*, only 55 are considered dangerous and of these only 4 were traditionally used by Central American tribes to coat their dart tips. Several of the poison dart frogs, however, secrete a poison that is considered one of the deadliest venoms ever identified. It has been calculated that one ounce of this poison could kill as many as 2.5 million people. Or, stated differently, the toxin of some species of these frogs is so strong that a mere 0.0000004 of an ounce is enough to kill a human being. Researchers have identified some 300 compounds in the secretions of these frogs and it is hoped that some will prove useful to humans in fighting diseases.

Bufo

Frogs and toads of all kinds carry slight amounts of protective poison. When the bufo was first introduced to Hawai'i in 1932, many dogs and cats sickened and even died from biting into its toxic skin, which is warted with small, poison-secreting glands. Survivors soon learned to keep away from these toads, which now squat in poised and unmolested confidence as they feed on roaches, centipedes and flying insects in our night yards. Poison from the bufo causes severe pain and vomiting in humans.

Japanese wrinkled frog

In 1896, a small, greenish gray frog called the Japanese wrinkled frog was brought from Japan and released in Makiki Stream in the hills behind Honolulu to help fight the war on mosquitoes. The descendants of this frog later spread to streams on several other islands. No research has been done to see if, after one hundred years, the wrinkled frog has evolved very different proteins or blood groups from its ancestors in Japan.

A tiny new intruder with a sleep-jarring croak is the latest immigrant amphibian to take up Hawai'i residence. This little tree

Tree frog

frog, called *Eleutherodactylus*, was probably a stowaway sneak-in by way of nursery plants and soil from the Caribbean. Measuring a mere one-half to one and one-half inches long, these frogs are remarkable in that their young skip the tadpole stage. Eggs, laid in loose soil and leaf litter, hatch directly to froglets in two to three weeks. They are remarkable as well for the noise they make: these new arrivals are causing disturbances on O'ahu, Maui and the Big Island. Their croaks sound out at a noise level of 90 to 100 decibels from a distance of eighteen inches. Compare this to a vacuum cleaner at 70 decibels or a rock band maxing out at 120 decibels—which is the threshold of pain. Doctors recommend earplugs with prolonged exposure to noise levels that exceed 90 decibels. During sleepless nights, one scientist finds comfort from such creaks and croaks by thinking historically:

Views

"Monotonous, insistent, inharmonious, the sounds that had kept me from falling off to sleep were also, I told myself, some of the most romantic and wonderful in the world of nature. Sounds much like these had probably been the first sounds made by voices of living

creatures in a hitherto largely silent world, when males of the earliest froglike amphibians began to gather together for mating and sought to lure the females to them with croaks and chirps. Before the first amphibians had emerged, there were, of course, inanimate noises—of the wind, of waves crashing on beaches, the roar of thunder, the rumble of volcanoes—but the only sounds produced by living creatures were the nonvocal ones of insects."

(D. Stivens, 1974)

Frogs and toads croak during mating time. The females appear more strongly drawn to loud, deep croaks, which are produced by older males whose voice boxes are larger. Scientists suspect that the more distinctive croaks identify these males as survivors that attract females, and their genes are thus passed on to the new pollywogs.

Just Wondering

Do female frogs and toads croak?

Warrior Mother

The Cockroach Wasp

Other Name: Jewel Wasp
Hawaiian Name:
Kopena ʻai ʻelelū
Scientific Name:
Ampulex compressa
Area of Origin: India
Date of Arrival: 1940

Arrival in Hawaiʻi

As we saw in earlier chapters, in days past sea ships, infested as they were with countless cockroaches, deposited them as scurrying stowaways onto the Hawaiian Islands with each call to port. Nineteen different kinds of roaches now live in Hawaiʻi. Humans react to roaches with revulsion and have brought in predator upon predator to combat them: the mynah bird, several small parasitic wasps, a variety of frogs and toads and—among the most beautiful and fascinating—the cockroach wasp. Three cockroach wasps were brought to Hawaiʻi in November, 1940, from Noumea, New Caledonia (Kanaky). As their name suggests, they are hunters of roaches, and thus valuable allies in people's efforts to reduce this pest's numbers.

Introducing a species' natural enemy to help reduce or eliminate it is a form of biological control that has been much used in Hawaiʻi: we bring in new species such as the cannibal snail, the bufo, and others to help solve problems caused by previous alien introductions. As a method, biological control is controversial. Some biologists feel that we should not further "pollute" the biological environment by bringing in new exotic species. The initial cost of biological control is high, but natural enemies then work for free forever. Often another method—chemical control—is used as a cheap, short-term alternative. Chemical control, however, brings its own set of problems and costs in the form of long-term effects, most of which are usually not fully understood.

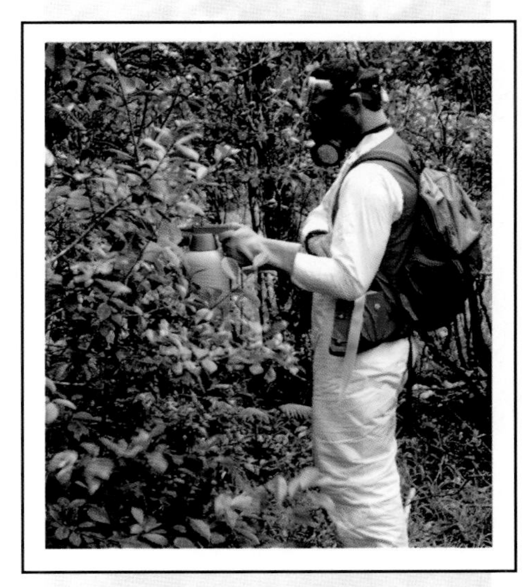

Chemical spraying

Food

Little is known about the feeding habits of the cockroach wasp. The first three immigrant wasps were fed honey during the long trip from Noumea. It is thought that cockroach wasps, like male mosquitoes, may feed on the minute droplets of nectar that are found on the surface of twigs and limbs. This and their own body fats may provide them all the energy they need.

Habitat

This is a restless wasp of a large size whose glittering blue-green body seems struck from the precious stones of its homeland India. These wasps are commonly seen skittering across the trunks of banyans, which house roaches in their many crevices.

The wasp's nervous body glints in the light as it zigzags up tree trunks, checking chinks and cracks in search of prey.

Reproduction

The female wasp is the hunter, the body-snatcher. Measuring nearly an inch in length, she alone engages in fierce wrestling with a roach that is often twice her size and several times her weight. In this way she procures an amazing womblike growth chamber in which her offspring live. In contrast to the quiet withdrawal behavior of many females, the cockroach wasp must serve her offspring first by entering into a mighty combat with an adversary that, in strength and agility, is her full measure. Only she is equipped with the stinger that first cripples then paralyzes the big red roaches. Grappling with the thrashing roach, its wings flitting, its body twisting and lurching, she finally grasps it, clasps it hard, clamps her jaws into the soft side of its flat body and sticks her stinger into its neck and chest. The venom partially disables the roach.

She then nips off the roach's antennae. It is possible that in severing the antennae, she disables the roach's sensory organs, thus further paralyzing it. To drag its body to a nearby nest site, she pulls on its antennae stumps or latches onto its mouth and backs her way into a chosen spot. The roach's legs often continue wriggling by reflex, providing a bit of forward mobility that helps the wasp lug her load.

The immobilized roach will serve as both food and shelter for a single wasp offspring. The female lays a slender white egg on the leg of the roach, hauls debris that covers the nest and departs, not to visit the site again.

Female cockroach wasp dragging a numbed roach

In three days the egg hatches. A tiny grub cuts and eats its way into the roach, which remains alive but senseless. The larva feeds on the roach's body in the days to come, slowly consuming the soft flesh within—like eating out the white part of a whole loaf of bread and leaving just the crust.

The chubby larva at this point is full-grown and nearly fills the hollow, criblike cavity of the roach. It pupates and spins a silk cocoon within this protective shell.

The cycle from egg to larva to pupa that is called metamorphosis has entered its final phase. In several weeks the full-grown wasp bites its way through the walls of its makeshift womb and emerges. One female wasp will kill about seventy roaches during her life.

The cockroach wasp is less frequently seen than it was just a few years ago. The insect-eating red-vented bulbul—a cage bird illegally released in the mid-1960s and now a common pest on O'ahu—may be the culprit. Scientists see a general decline in the biodiversity of many habitats where numerous insect species, including the cockroach wasp, previously interacted.

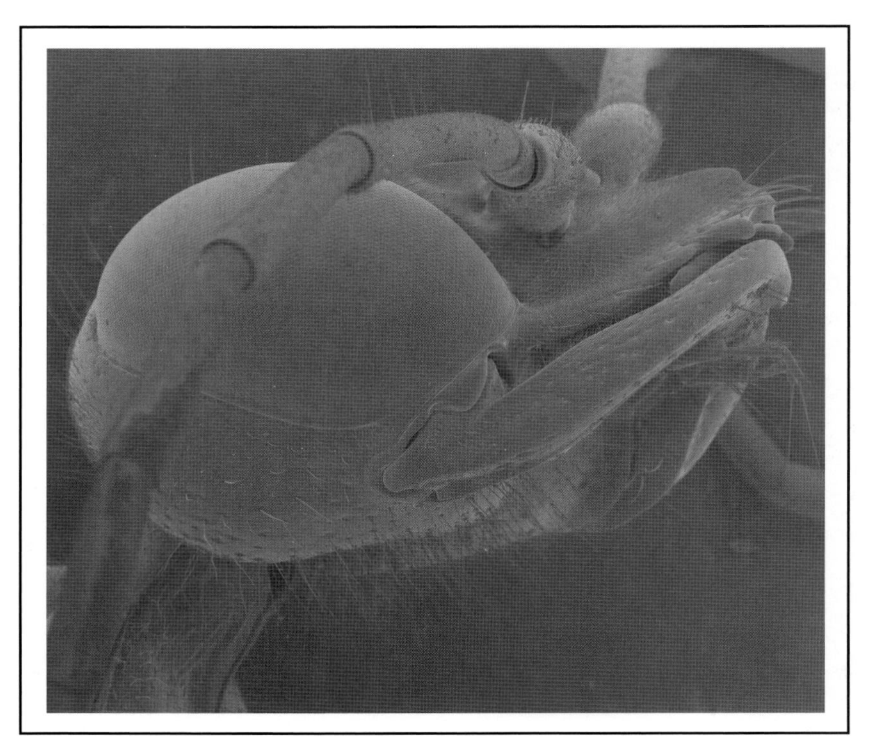

Cockroach wasp head, magnified 20 times

More Cockroach Wasp Facts

There are more than a thousand species of wasps in Hawai'i, a good half of which are endemic. Very few have been studied. Scientists currently have their hands full just identifying new species. Wasps, like all insects, belong to the group of invertebrates called "arthropods," a Greek word that refers to their jointed or segmented legs. This group includes such familiar animals in Hawai'i as spiders, scorpions, centipedes, millipedes, shrimp, crayfish and crabs. It is thought that there are some 10 to 30 million different arthropods on the Earth. Only about a million of these have been described. In Hawai'i, no more than half of all our native species of insects have even been given names!

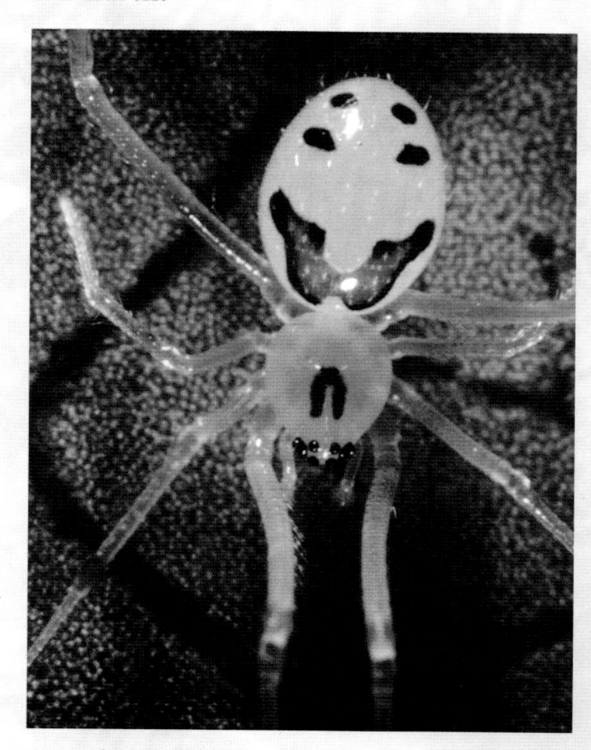

Happyface spider hides under leaves from birds in Hawaiian forests. This spider catches prey like flies and leafhoppers by kicking out a silk lasso. This half-inch spider is common on five islands and symbolizes the exciting ten thousand kinds of miniwildlife in Hawaiian forests.

Just Wondering

Spiders are among the more common and—to some humans—creepy arthropods that share our homes and yards. Much, however, remains a mystery as to how spiders live their lives. Entomologists, for example, can't seem to agree on this basic and important question: Why don't spiders get stuck in their own webs?

It is estimated that there may be somewhere between 25 and 35 million nonplant life forms on the planet today. Only about a million and a half of these animal species have been identified by scientists. These animals break down into the following groups. Note the numerical importance of the arthropods.

4,000 mammals
9,000 birds
6,000 reptiles
3,000 amphibians
20,000 fish
80,000 mollusks
(shellfish, octopuses and squids)
4,000 echinoderms
(starfish and sea urchins)
923,000 arthropods
(insects, spiders, scorpions and crustaceans)
9,000 coelenterates
(jellyfish, sea anemones and corals)
66,000 lower forms
(worms and microbes)

Another important arthropod in Hawai'i, though very different from the cockroach wasp, is the honeybee. In 1852, an attempt was made to bring in the first honeybees by ship around Cape Horn from New England. All went well until the vessel entered the tropics on the Atlantic side. Heat onboard caused the wax comb to melt. The bees suffocated. Other attempts were made and a reward of $10 offered, but it took a good five years before four hives from California were finally landed in Honolulu. They were placed in the area in lower Nu'uanu Valley that today is called Foster Gardens. Soon new colonies swarmed off into the adjoining valleys. Hawaiian *kiawe* honey in short time became renowned for its particular fragrant whiteness and was found as far away as the bread slices of London.

Views

"Bees—It has come to our attention that there are a great number of bees here in our valleys. In Kalihi, there are many bees in the hollows of trees. Honey has been gotten and it's as good as the Kona honey which we've had here. These however are wild bees."

(Nūpepa Kū'oko'a, *September, 1865, trans. author)*

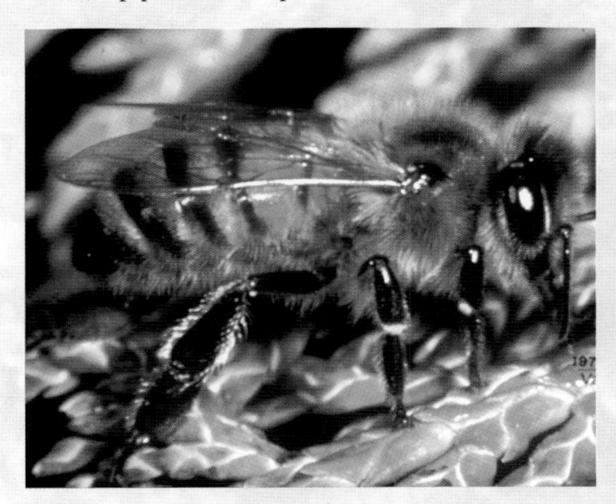

Honeybee

"Bees of the Forest—There are lots of bees here in the mountains of O'ahu. We have frequently seen the buckets full of honey that the haole *Okamu has gotten in upper Mānoa and Kalihi. It is furthermore said that there is also a great deal in the mountains of Ko'olau. Friends, you really should try this honey. It is great together with bread."*

(Nūpepa Kū'oko'a, *November, 1865, trans. author)*

A second introduced wasp that helps to keep roach numbers in Hawai'i at a bearable level is called the ensign wasp. "Ensign" is a synonym for "flag" or "banner." The word is used with this wasp because of the way its raised abdomen continually waves up and down like the checkered flag at the finish line of an auto race. The wasp bobs and wobbles about, nervously approaching roach egg cases in which it will insert its own tiny eggs. The larvae of the ensign wasp feed on the cockroach larvae. Ensign wasps can frequently be seen in and around our houses in Hawai'i, where they find the beanlike roach satchels.

The ensign wasp is one of about 240 species of alien wasps that have been introduced by people to Hawai'i for biological pest control. Of these about 175 species have become established. Another 400 species of wasps have sneaked into the islands through accidental human transport.

One such uninvited guest is a very aggressive species that probably entered Hawai'i as a stowaway on untreated Christmas trees

Female centipede with young

from the mainland. This fierce yellowjacket became established in the early 1970s and is thought to have played a major role in the decline of many native arthropods, and possibly native birds as well. But perhaps the most threatening of the alien arthropods introduced to Hawai'i are the forty-two species of ants that now live in this land that was once free of such insects altogether. Ants are implicated in the extinction of many native Hawaiian species.

At current count, some 3,400 species of alien arthropods have been introduced to Hawai'i, either intentionally or unintentionally. The rate of arrival is about two dozen new species per year.

Just Wondering

Can we go back with our mind's eye and see a Hawai'i before the countless alien introductions brought in by humans? Can we imagine a Hawai'i with no ants, no centipedes, no scorpions, no roaches or rats, or mosquitoes? Some sixty species of foreign birds have established breeding populations in the lowland areas where humans live. With our wonder, can we hear the song of the land as the old birds sang it?

TERRITORIALITY: *KAPU*—KEEP OUT

The Tilapia

Hawaiian Name: *Kilapia*
Scientific Name: *Tilapia mossambica*
Area of Origin: Africa
Date of Arrival: 1951

An undisturbed school of tilapia presents a slow salt-and-pepper busyness. Females show shades of gray, males a range of blacks. Like that of the gecko, tilapia coloration shifts as the fishes' bodies adapt to the darker or lighter tones of their background. With the male, a series of color changes accompanies the stages of the reproductive cycle as well. A spawning male is dark black with attractive red trim. The tilapia also camouflages its presence depending on the depth and color of the water that surrounds it. In the extremely polluted Ala Wai Canal in Waikīkī, tilapia are dark, greenish brown; in clear irrigation ditches they are a steely gray.

Tilapia color adapts to its background.

ARRIVAL IN HAWAIʻI

The common tilapia was introduced to Oʻahu first in 1951 to rid plantation ditches of algae. In 1962, another member of this family, the black-chinned tilapia, was introduced from West Africa by the National Marine Fisheries Service. It was hoped that this species would provide a handy bait fish for commercial *aku* (skipjack tuna) fishermen who pole fish off sampans. The black-chinned tilapia were kept in holding tanks in Honolulu Harbor. In an incident reminiscent of the dumping of the first mosquito wrigglers out of water casks into Lahaina Stream in 1826, they

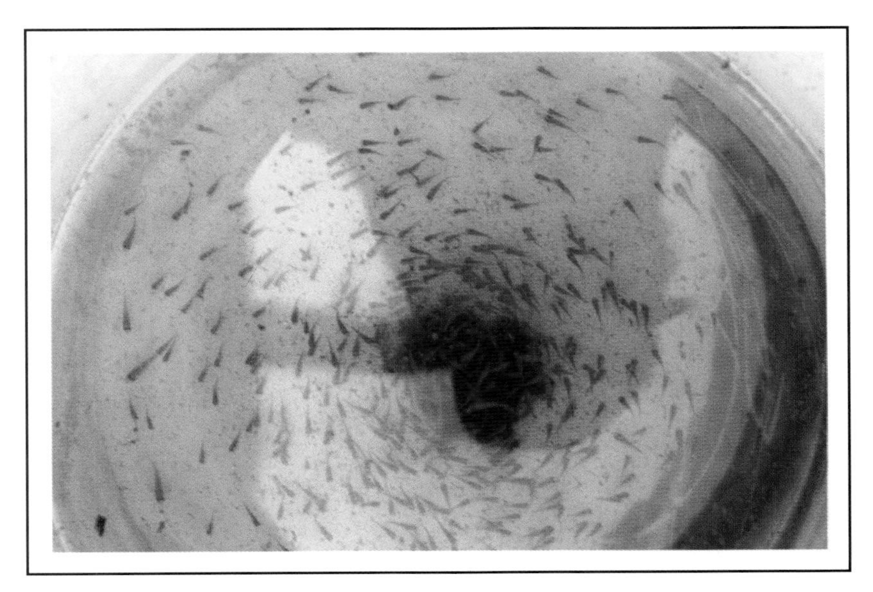

Tilapia fry in holding tank

were accidentally washed into the harbor when water was drained from their tanks.

Habitat

Several types of tilapia, all originally from Africa, where they are an important food source, now live in streams, reservoirs and coastal waters statewide in Hawai'i. The common tilapia have taken well to the warm water of plantation ditches. They breed year-round, and have become abundant. The native habitats of tilapia in Africa contain high levels of salt; tilapia in Hawai'i, therefore, can tolerate salt concentrations that would kill other freshwater fish. The black-chinned tilapia are now commonly seen in the lower reaches of streams, where fresh water slows and warms on its way to the sea; in the brackish estuary zones; and out farther, forming floating schools in saltwater areas offshore. Tilapia are even spreading around the reef line of O'ahu, where they are easily caught by throw-net.

Food

These fish are mostly herbivorous and have big appetites. When first introduced, tilapia quickly unclogged plantation ditches: water flowed clear and clean to cane and pineapple. In earlier days, ditch upkeep was a drudgery of frequent bottom dredgings using horse-drawn chains and buckets. Later, chemicals were used without much concern for their long-term effects. Tilapia were seen as an easy and environmentally gentle solution to keeping water flowing to important cash crops.

However, they can do too good a job eating out water plants. Schools of tilapia are often seen hovering high in a pond or stream, their many little round mouths like cookie-cutters cutting through the murky surface as they gulp air. This is an indication that the water is low in oxygen. The tilapia make do by drawing oxygen directly from the surface air. Many times the tilapia themselves have caused the problem by eating out the very plants that produce oxygen and keep the water habitat in balance.

Tilapia near the surface gulp for air.

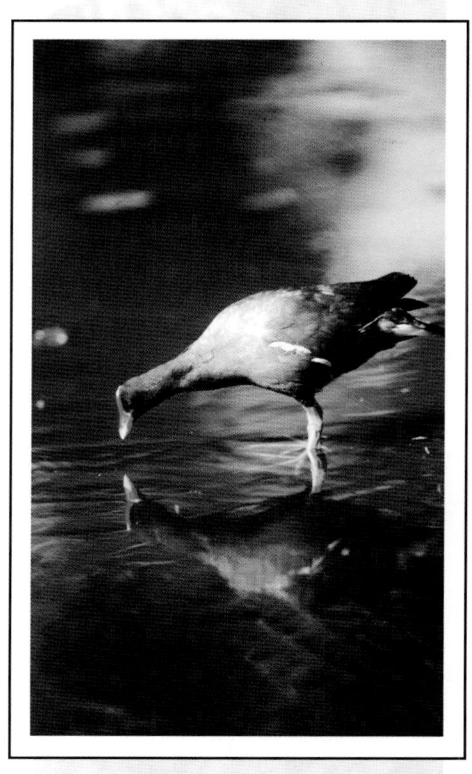

Hawaiian mudhen

It is now clear that tilapia compete for food with native water birds, four of which are endangered. Federal biologists working on Maui and Kaua'i say that large schools of tilapia living in marshlands on these islands feed on the same plants as Hawaiian coots, ducks and mudhens and also eat insects that provide food to native stilts.

Hawaiian stilts

Views

"At the start of the breeding season animals perform their most extraordinary displays. They leap, dance, twist and turn. They ruffle their feathers, bristle their hair, erect their spines and puff up their pouches. Their previously dull bodies suddenly flash and glisten with bright colors and vivid contrasts. They strut and weave, nod and twitch, and generally behave with such fire and intensity that the animal-watcher can only marvel at the richness of the scenes unfolding before him."

(D. Morris, 1990)

Tilapia reproduction is fascinating to study, as it involves intense territorial skirmishing and nest building, elaborate courtship and, for a fish, unusual attention to offspring. At each stage of the breeding cycle, the color of the male darkens, culminating in the deep velvety black color of the spawn.

Males are territorial. As they fight, their bodies remain dark. When one withdraws from the skirmishing, pullback is signaled with a color change, his body switching to a dirty ashen gray. Egg-bearing females assume a rain-gray hue.

Male tilapia

Having secured his territory, the male makes a nest on the bottom by stirring and nudging away debris and shaping a crater with his strong jaws. He is testy and ever active, fanning clean his nest, chasing away intruders, curving gracefully outward, prodding a passing female to his saucer-size nest. His body has now gone a bold charcoal black with traces of blue stripes and a first etching of red along fin lines.

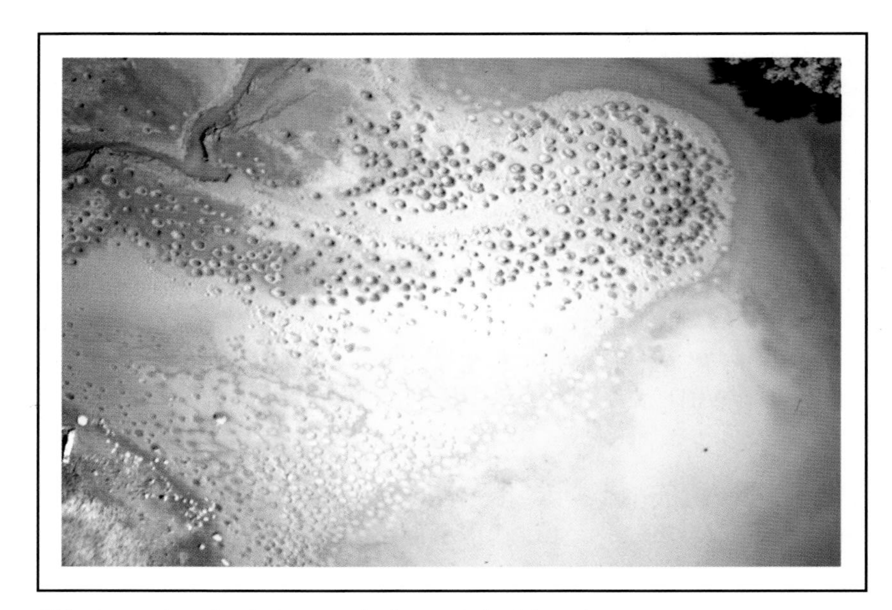

Tilapia nesting site drying out during period of drought

Drying mud cakes and cracks where tilapia fry once swam. Note dried-up fry.

A female is coaxed in close and lays up to one hundred eggs in the nest. The male, in his most splendid breeding colorations, passes down over the eggs and fertilizes them.

Just Wondering

Sex . . . what's it all about, anyway? If the main biological purpose of life is to create more life, to pass on one's own genes to a new generation, then why don't animals just clone themselves? It would seem a much more efficient and economic way of assuring one's survival as a species, without the dangers and difficulties and—for humans—expense that courtship and sex bring. Why all the fuss of sex?

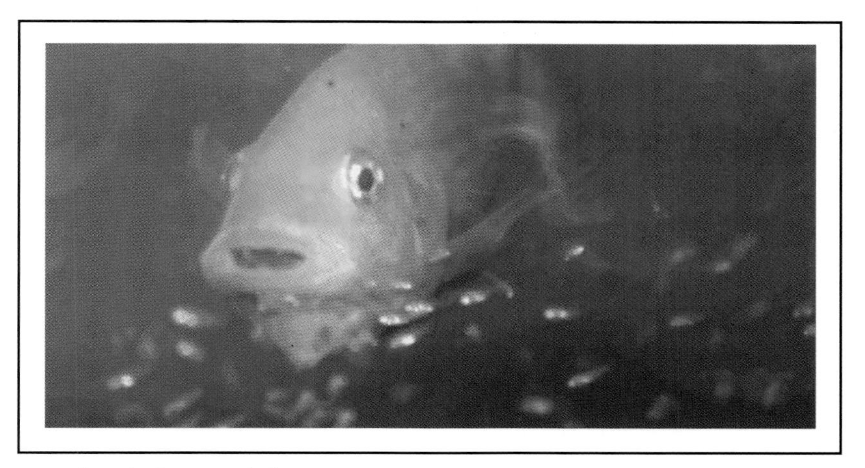

Female red tilapia with fry

Then the pale female tilts down, sucks up the eggs one by one, clustering them into her bulging mouth. She carries them for several days until they hatch, rearranging them from time to time with slight chewing movements, keeping them aerated. She does not eat during the incubation period.

The fry hatch in a hazy mist of quivering minnows. They hover in close to the female's gill slits and cheeks. Like the joey of the rock wallaby retreating quickly into its mother's pouch, at the slightest hint of danger the fry dart back to her mouth, where she holds them until the threat has passed.

For five to eight days the silvery cloud of minnows glistens about the solitary female. Eventually the cloud drifts off. The mother moves away. Her parenting has come to an end.

Just Wondering

The misty blur of quivering minnows is an example of a species' strategy of finding safety in numbers. What advantages do herding, flocking, swimming, or swarming together bring when a predator approaches?

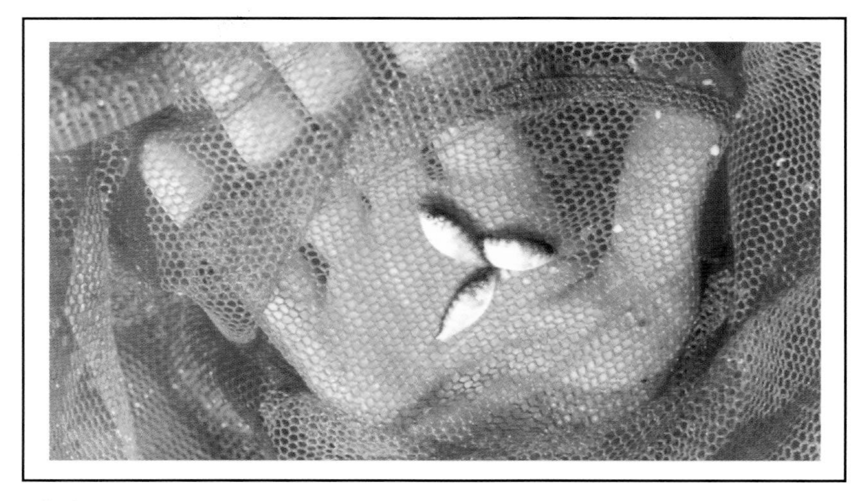

The big ones got away.

More Tilapia Facts

A major predator of the tilapia in Hawai'i, the native barracuda, is also a camouflage artist as it awaits its prey. The barracuda's lean, silvery body hangs motionless in its shimmering, sun-filled habitat. Dark above and darkly striped below, it easily blends with its surroundings, unseen by its prey, the tilapia.

»»»»»»»»»»»»

A number of native Hawaiian ocean fish are as adaptable to fresh water as tilapia are to salt water, including the *'ama'ama* (mullet), the *pāpio* (young jack) and the *āholehole.* Several types of *limu,* particularly the *manauea,* or *ogo* variety, thrive where freshwater springs gush up and mix with sea water. These areas of mixing waters, some along the coast, others inland, were much prized in the past. The brackish mix promoted the growth of algae, which quickly fattened captive fish.

»»»»»»»»»»»»

Not a lot is known about the effects of tilapia on native freshwater stream life in Hawai'i. It is a fact, however, that several Kaua'i streams where bass were introduced earlier this century have lost many of their native species. Numerous freshwater animals, such as the *'o'opu wai* (goby), follow what is called an amphidromous life cycle. Reproduction begins in fresh water; the larvae then wash seaward and develop in salt water while drifting in the open ocean. Offspring later reenter a freshwater habitat when they travel up mountain streams as juveniles or adults. Dense schools of tilapia, cluttered at the mouths of such streams, may interfere with the safe passage of these returning species.

»»»»»»»»»»»»

The tilapia is one of many animals we have introduced to Hawai'i without having a complete knowledge of their possible impact on native habitats. Other examples include the mongoose, brought in to kill rats, but whose fierce appetite quickly turned to ground-nesting native birds, and the cannibal snail, which was imported to kill African snails but has done such terrible damage to Hawaiian tree snails.

»»»»»»»»»»»»

Tilapia are a valuable food in many countries, efficiently converting algae to a tasty source of protein for people. In Asia and East Africa, tilapia are kept in backyard ponds, where they are raised for family meals. Several aquaculture projects in Hawai'i are developing easy and cheap methods for cultivating this fish. A major project in Wai'anae uses a type of tilapia with a yellowish skin. To encourage people who don't normally eat tilapia to try these aquaculture products, they have been renamed the "Wai'anae sunfish." The tilapia, each averaging a pound and more, is good to eat when grown in clean water. On O'ahu, it is sold in Chinatown, where it is kept live in big tanks. In California, tilapia filets are commonly sold in supermarkets.

»»»»»»»»»»»»

Backyard aquaculture

Ready for market

Tilapia are providing second chances to at-risk teens who have found that a whole day at high school is not where they want to be. Through an alternative community program, about twenty-five Leeward O'ahu students are raising taro and tilapia and harvesting additional skills as well in farming, aquaculture and marketing. They are also developing personal skills that will help them in their lives—for starters, hopefully, to stay in school and off the streets.

Views

"I was always getting into fights, then getting suspended. Then I would get into another beef and get suspended again. . . . Auntie is strict but that's what some of us needed. When she found out one of her students is cutting class instead of actually being sick, she calls and makes sure he or she came to school. This place has taught me about discipline, responsibility. I'm not afraid to say that without it, I wouldn't still be in school."

(Angel Asuncion, student, Wai'anae Coast Community Alternative Development Corp., Honolulu Advertiser, *October 28, 1998)*

Just Wondering

Will we act as responsible stewards of the many organisms that share the Earth with us? Could a thoughtful stewardship of the land provide us more positive relationships with each other and greater meaning to our own lives?

Catch of the day

Aloha ʻĀina: Responsible Stewardship

Views

"In a reasonable world, men would have treated these islands as precious possessions, as natural museums filled with beautiful and curious works of creation, valuable beyond price, because nowhere in the world are they duplicated."

(Rachel Carson, author)

In the land that lies about us, little is left of old Hawaiʻi. Many of her "beautiful and curious works of creation" are gone forever. Tourists coming to these islands are greeted by a gracious but artificial landscape, a hodgepodge patchwork of plants and animals brought here from all over the world. Children growing up in Hawaiʻi are hard-pressed to recognize our most common endemic plants. Even the great encircling sea, so vast and seemingly indestructible, now suffers terribly from human abuse.

Beginning with the arrival of the first Polynesian canoes, different peoples at different times have carried countless new species to Hawaiʻi. The list of animals reads on and on like the inventory of some large city zoo: pigs and flies from Polynesia, mongooses and mynah birds from India; catfish and wrinkled frogs from Asia; Kentucky cardinals and

monarch butterflies from North America; bufos, mosquitoes and centipedes from Mexico; ladybugs and wallabies from Australia; tilapia and Jackson's chameleons from Africa; guppies and swordtails from South America . . .

A similar list could be drawn up of the more than four thousand plants that have been introduced to Hawai'i. Of the flowers that color our yards and bear fruit to feed us, nearly all are introduced varieties.

Even the perfumed *lei* we offer—the joyous symbols of our *aloha*—are strung with mostly "foreign" flowers: ginger, carnation, orchid, crown flower, *pīkake*, *pakalana*, plumeria . . .

Yet through our use of these flowers in our practice of *aloha*, we have given them a value in their own right, not because of where they have come from, but because of what they have come to mean to us. By a kind of cultural evolution, they have become part of our precious cultural habitat, our sense of place.

It is the same with the foods we grow up loving: the *lomilomi* salmon, shave ice, *sushi*, *malasada*, *manapua*, *kim chee*, *bibinka*, sweet bread, salty seed, pickled mango, *kalbi* chicken, and many other scrumptious goodies—all of which have come from far-off places.

And it is the same with the many bloods that give our bodies their very life—bloods from the far-off lands of our immigrant ancestors: the Marquesas Islands, America, China, Japan, Portugal, Korea, Vietnam, Samoa . . .

What has come from afar now makes up who we are, together today, and what we love about our Hawai'i.

Yet, at the same time, it matters greatly that exotic species have taken over virtually every Hawaiian habitat from sea level to the summits of the highest mountains.

Many endemic Hawaiian species have vanished forever. Forever. It is mostly in the remotest places where human development has not spread—the thickest forest, the highest, steepest sea cliff, the most unwelcoming cinder crater—that endemic Hawaiian plants and animals still hang on.

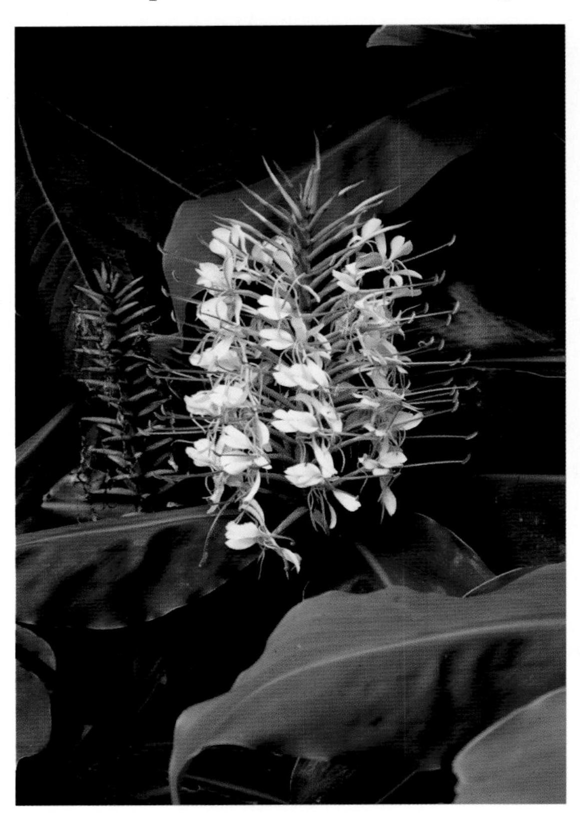

Kāhili ginger: beautiful, fragrant, environmentally disastrous

So what should we do about the fragrant *kāhili* ginger that clogs native woods? The bristly boar that churns up rain forest floors? Or the bright red cardinal that sings its heart out in Hawaiian morning sunshine and then is off to compete aggressively with native birds?

In the swirl of competing needs and allegiances there are few simple, straight answers. It is easy for us to feel confused, to despair and grow angry at losses that seem so grim, so overwhelming. So forever.

But, there are some things we do know: We know that it is man the disrupter who must try to make right. We know we must become much more aware and appreciative of the uniqueness of our homeland's natural heritage. There is still much we can preserve; there is much that can heal. But the survival of hundreds of endangered species now requires human intervention. Now. To intervene appropriately, we must learn much more about native habitats and the species they support. Now!

Views

"[A]ll these little creatures around us were here long before us . . . , so they're the really true Hawaiians. I feel very sad when I look around and find that the forest is disappearing, because it's the true Hawaiians that was here before us that are disappearing, and after they go then we go next. . . . [S]o the erosion process, you know, it's happening and we can see it happening. But we can stop it. And this is where we stop it: we stop it by teaching our children to be sensitive to the creatures, to the plants around us. . . . So if they live, we live."

(Pualani Kanahele, Kumu Hula, Hālau o Kekuhi, quoted in "Listen to the Forest" by Eddie and Myrna Kamae, 1991)

Our endemic plants and animals are the precious treasures of our Hawaiian natural heritage. Found nowhere else in the world, they deserve our special awareness; imperiled as they are, they demand our care and our concern.

We must take what we have been given and try to make the right choices that will safeguard what is left. Now and forever. What we do now is important: small changes made by many people can make a big difference. We must become the good stewards of this land; if we begin now to

Transporting alien species by foot

. . . by dung

treat these life forms as precious possessions, we will have them forever.

Views

"We have lost a great deal, and we'll lose more species before we've slowed the rate. . . . But nearly half of Hawai'i's original native ecosystems are still here, harboring thousands of endemic plant and animal species. And moreover, we now have or are developing the tools to protect the rest."

(Alan Holt, Former Director of Science and Stewardship, The Nature Conservancy of Hawai'i. Quoted in the Nature Conservancy News, *Feb.–March, 1987)*

Though it recounts a sad story, and laments that much has been lost, this book is not about bad guys. There is no blame here. Every species is, in the greater scheme of all things living, singular and, as such, sacred. The animals presented are therefore considered with as much detached

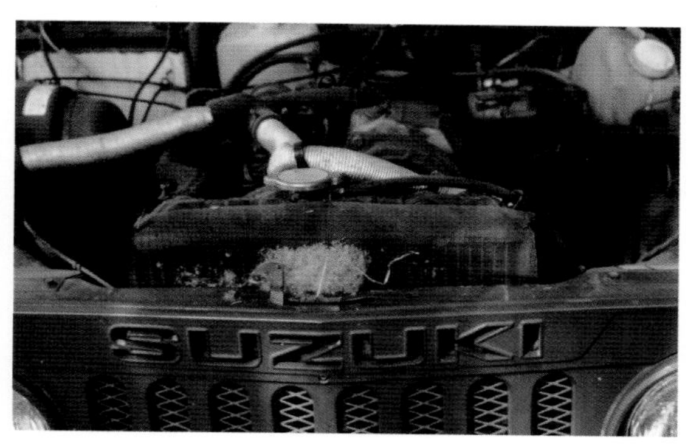

. . . by car

wonder and reverence as possible, despite an awareness that, in the more narrowly defined context of a given native habitat, a particular species may have wreaked havoc on a unique Hawaiian ecosystem. Once and again in the study of natural history, one is humbly reminded that, from the cosmic perspective, Mother Nature is quite indifferent to the fact that one or the other of her many splendid creations is perishing. Stewardship is a human responsibility.

The last section of this book is about two people who are trying to make right choices, whose small changes are making a big difference. People who are committed to *aloha ʻāina*, good stewardship.

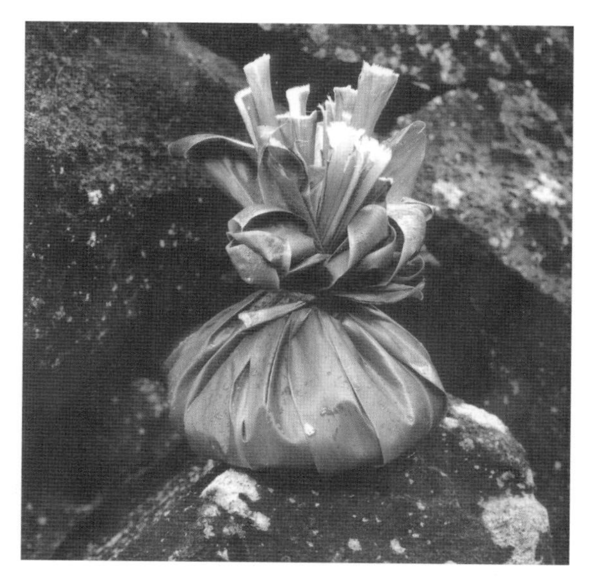

E aloha ʻāina kākou! *Let us love the land!*

Defending Her Land: Cynthia Salley

Views

"Frankly, if it wasn't for her interest in the problem [of Hawaiian crows], there probably wouldn't have been any wild species."

(Alan Lieberman, Program Director, the Peregrine Fund, Honolulu Star-Bulletin, *June 9, 1998)*

Cynthia Salley

As the chapter on the Hawaiian crow indicates, the list of environmental factors contributing to the decline of the *'alalā* is sadly long. But it is not just the environmental disturbances that are the source of struggles and setbacks. Add to these the political and legal battles that festered around this precious and rare bird throughout the early part of the 1990s and it becomes clear how difficult the recovery of an endangered species can be. In their passionate and panicky efforts to save this failing species, people have clashed bitterly over what approach to take and how to take it.

At the flash point for these battles has been a single, strong-minded woman, Cynthia Salley. Part-owner of the 60,000-acre McCandless Ranch in Kona, on the island of Hawai'i, Salley knows her land well. Her ranch contains some of the best-preserved native forest areas in Hawai'i—tens of thousands of acres of protected Hawaiian habitat that might just be the last hope left for the few remaining Hawaiian crows. In agreement with many scientists,

'Alalā *enclosure, McCandless Ranch, Kona, island of Hawai'i*

Salley sees the decline of an endemic species as the result of multiple environmental disruptions, the most important being mosquito-borne diseases: to fix the species, fix the habitat. At one time, Salley also felt that biologists were being overly aggressive in their research methods, especially during the *'alalā* breeding season, and were doing more harm than good. So she put a *kapu* on her ranch, shutting down human access to this last flock of unique Hawaiian crows.

In the early 1990s, with *'alalā* numbers dropping precariously, pressures to get at these last birds increased. In 1996, The Audubon Society filed suit against the U.S. Fish and Wildlife Service to force them to act in accordance with federal laws designed to support endangered species. In the face of a stubborn refusal by the McCandless Ranch to allow access to the remaining wild birds, The Audubon Society felt that only federal intervention would offer hope for *'alalā* recovery.

Views

***"The owners . . . recently announced plans for 'salvage' logging of* koa *trees in an area designated as essential habitat for the* 'alalā *and three other endangered species. . . . As yet no tropical forest ecosystem biologist has been able to review the logging plan to see if it is compatible with the continued existence of the crow. However, it is known that the ranch owners plan to harvest mature, dead, and dying* koa *trees, and it is precisely those trees that are utilized by the* 'alalā.**

('Elepaio, *Newsletter of the Hawai'i Audubon Society, May, 1996)*

Salley held her ground. She wouldn't allow field biologists into the area to study the *'alalā*, insisting that more harm than good would come of it and that such human disturbance could very well spell the end of the small flock.

Finally, with the help of a thorough study by the National Academy of Sciences, a compromise was struck: scientists were allowed to take eggs for captive rearing, but live birds were to be left alone. The compromise led to a partnership among several interested groups who found a way to work toward the shared goal of assuring this critically rare bird a future.

Cynthia Salley is hopeful:

Views

"Through the years, considering the fact that this partnership was initiated by a law suit, we have come through a lot of problems and come to a place of trust and understanding. We've come a long way."

(Cynthia Salley, Honolulu Advertiser, *November, 1997)*

That trust is one key to the recovery program that is now under way. It is called captive breeding, and it imitates what takes place in nature when nesting *'alalā* face a crisis.

When disaster strikes an *'alalā* nest, nature has a marvelous backup plan. If for some reason the first clutch of eggs is

Eggs for captive rearing

Hungry ʻalalā *chicks*

Crow-shaped hand puppet

lost—to a storm, a rat, a cat, a fire—crows, like other birds, will often renest and lay a second clutch, thus assuring a batch of offspring for the year. Scientists are taking advantage of this in captive breeding programs on Maui and the Big Island, prodding more precious eggs out of the very few females left. The procedure is called multiple clutching, and so far, results are promising. In 1997, ten *ʻalalā* eggs were hatched—more than ever before in captivity—offering a very modest hope of survival for these critically rare birds. Ten *ʻalalā* nestlings is nearly one-third the total current population of the Hawaiian crow.

But hatching is only the start. Like premature human babies in incubators, newborn chicks require constant care. Everything is monitored. Everything is controlled. The chick receives hourly feedings from a crow-shaped hand puppet that reaches down to deposit food in its gaping mouth. Delicate stages of hand-feeding, imprinting and release must follow.

And once they are set loose into the highlands of the McCandless Ranch, the "real world" out there provides numerous threats that *ʻalalā* never faced during a very sheltered childhood in captivity.

In the spring of 1998, for example, five *ʻalalā*—all of them raised in captivity—

The chick is hand-fed, using the puppet.

were killed by two marauding hawks on the McCandless Ranch, a terrible but typical setback for a program having to find its way forward each hard step of the way. The two culprit hawks were caught and moved more than halfway across the island to Hawaiʻi Volcanoes National Park, only to reappear within a month. Three more *ʻalalā* were taken by these hawks in September. By the summer of 1999, only two *ʻalalā* remained in the wild. There may be more to it than just one endemic species preying on another:

Views

"Since we have seen a variety of infections in the* ʻalalā *lately, it is possible that these birds were too sick to be able to fend off* ʻio *attacks. Although it's easy to point the finger at the* ʻio *as the sole culprit, we should not jump to that conclusion. It may very well be a combination of factors; for instance, we know that one bird died recently from a disease transmitted by feral cats."

(Robert P. Smith, Pacific Islands Manager for the U.S. Fish and Wildlife Service, ʻElepaio, *Newsletter of the Hawaiʻi Audubon Society, November, 1998)*

Now the question that Cynthia Salley and other researchers are struggling with is how do humans teach *ʻalalā* youngsters hawk survival skills that they should be picking up through their socialization process with the flock? Setting out the human-reared crows in huge aviaries within the wild habitat may be part of the solution. Caged *ʻalalā* can observe the wild birds, hear them, and watch them deal with problems such as hawks. Or should the problem be turned around: how to teach the hawks not to include the endangered crow in their diet?

Meanwhile, Salley continues to take a strong stand concerning the roles and the rights of private landowners when confronted with government or private programs in support of endangered species. Many landowners don't want the hassle and responsibility that come with cooperating in such programs, including the costly threat of lawsuits. In extreme cases, a landowner has been accused of purposely destroying a species or its habitat to avoid putting up with such hassles.

But, argues Cynthia Salley, if native habitat restoration and preservation are the keys to saving an endemic species that faces extinction, then private landowners are crucial players and must be meaningfully included in any solution.

Views

"We need to work together and respect the right to make a living. If you want success, you've got to take out the threats of law suits. Unless they [the ranchers] can get incentives on the land, it's going to be shoot, shovel and shut up."

(Cynthia Salley, Honolulu Star-Bulletin, *June 9, 1998)*

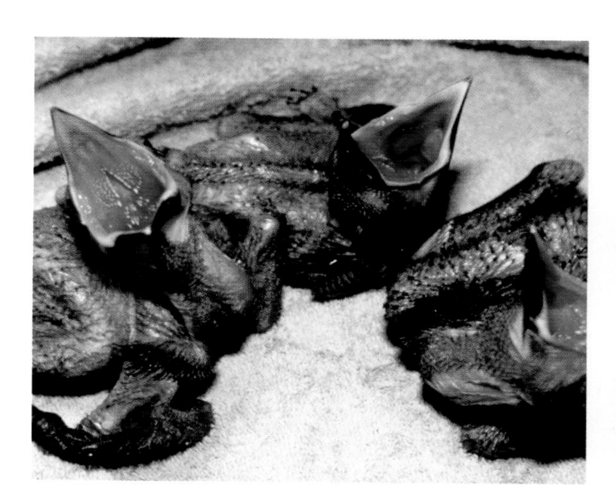

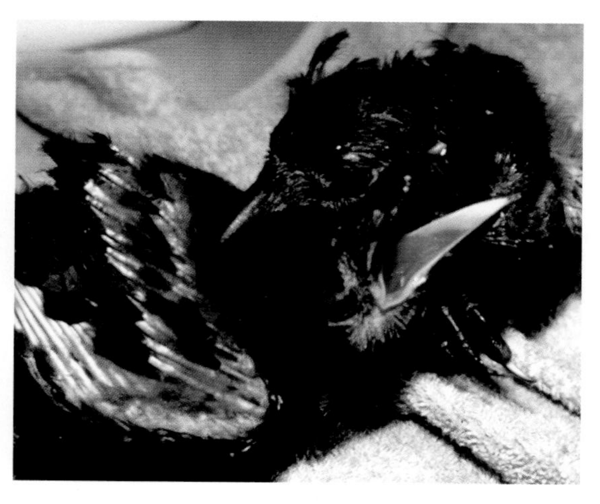

Captive-bred and cheeping for survival

Celebrating Life's Voyage: Nainoa Thompson

Views

"These midges can fly through mosquito netting two abreast, and would change the living patterns of Hawai'i's residents. . . . There are many more [pests] out there waiting for a chance to come in."

(Francis Howarth, entomologist, Bishop Museum, Honolulu Star-Bulletin, *May 4, 1995)*

Nainoa Thompson

In 1995, a stowaway fly the size of a pinhead succeeded in delaying the joyful arrival of six Polynesian voyaging canoes and their escort boats to Hilo Harbor. Good thinking prevented an environmental disaster for Hawai'i.

When one of the crew members onboard the *Hawai'i Loa* reported welts and itching on his skin, master navigator Nainoa Thompson grew concerned. A radio message to staff members at The Nature Conservancy of Hawai'i and consultation with insect experts at the Bishop Museum confirmed his fears.

The stowaway pest, called the *no-no* throughout the Pacific, was to be taken very seriously. It was guessed to be the relative of a similar tiny biting fly, unknown in Hawai'i, that had effectively stopped construction of hotels and whole resorts in Florida and on Caribbean Islands. Clouds of these "no-see-um" gnats could take a big bite out of human enjoyment of Hawaiian beaches forever, inflicting as many as ten thousand itching, festering bites on a person in one day.

There would be no celebration. Yet. Instead, every precaution had to be taken to prevent the introduction of this biting midge to the islands. The canoes dropped sail and came to a glum standstill some hundred miles from shore—far enough away to reduce the chance of windblown flies reaching land. A Coast Guard C-130 took off from Honolulu to drop canisters of insecticide to the waiting canoes. The crew scrubbed and spray-fogged their quarters and dumped all fruit and vegetables into the sea, including a valuable collection of breadfruit saplings from the South Pacific.

Fumigation instead of celebration. It was an unexpected end to a grand and long-planned adventure by Pacific island peoples who had worked together for years in preparation for this voyage and who rejoiced in their shared cultural heritage.

But on another, more lasting level, it was a celebration, a wonderful triumph of what is best in the human spirit. Humans on these little canoes had placed a concern for the long-term well-being of the land above a concern for self. Nainoa and his crew had educated themselves to understand just how destructive certain alien species introductions can be to Hawai'i. The biting midge, for example, would have caused great harm to this environment. Nainoa grasped immediately what could happen if the canoes continued into Hilo Harbor. He acted to prevent a disaster. One person making a difference.

Views

"Each time we lose another Hawaiian plant or bird or insect or forest, we lose a living part of our ancient culture. Stopping alien pests is about choosing our future and saving our past."

(Nainoa Thompson, master navigator; Polynesian Voyaging Society Website: www.hokulea.net)

So many times in Hawai'i's past, people carelessly, selfishly or just unknowingly have brought in new species of plants and animals with too little thought to the lasting consequences of their actions for this beloved *'āina*: rats hidden in Polynesian canoes, cattle let loose in Kona, centipedes shoveled onshore in unwanted ballast on the wharf in Honolulu, mosquito wrigglers dumped into a Lahaina stream, rabbits released on Laysan Island,

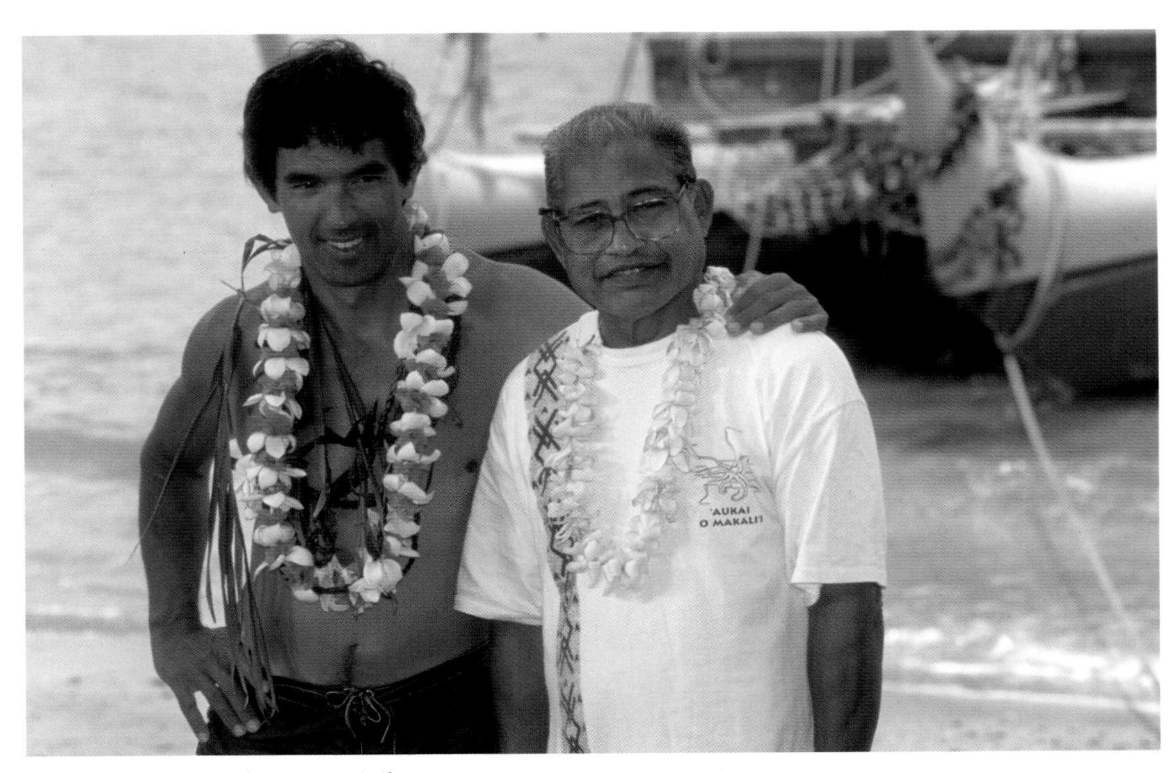

Nainoa with his teacher, Mau Piailug

mongooses in Hāmākua, mynahs and guppies in Moanalua, bulbuls in Makiki, banana poka, miconia, iguana, piranha . . .

Nainoa and his crew chose the land as the lasting value. Their choice reminds us that what we do as individuals is important. It is people, acting as responsible stewards of the land, who will assure the lasting celebration of life's great voyage on our planet Earth.

He ali'i ka 'āina,
He kauā ke kanaka.

The Land is a chief,
Man is a steward.
(Old Hawaiian saying)

Hawaiian Glossary

The Hawaiian orthography used in this book is in accordance with current usage as indicated by the most recent edition of the Puku'i-Elbert Hawaiian dictionary (1986) and the revised guidelines of 'Ahahui 'Ōlelo Hawai'i (1978).

āholehole bright silver endemic fish common in tidepools and along coasts

aia there is, there are

'āina land, earth, country

'akolika ostrich

aku skipjack tuna

'alalā Hawaiian crow

ali'i chief, chiefess, ruler, monarch

aloha 'āina love or reverence for the land

'ama'ama mullet of a medium size

'anae mullet of a large size

auē much used interjection, both good and bad: Oh! Gee! Wow!

'aumakua family or personal god

awa milkfish

'awa lightly alcoholic beverage from *'awa* root used in ceremony

eia here is, here are

'elelū cockroach

haole foreigner, non-Hawaiian, Caucasian

he a, an

hiwahiwa precious; used to refer to fully black pigs offered to gods

honu turtle, sea turtle

ho'oilo rainy part of the Hawaiian year, November to May

hua egg, fruit

'ie'ie endemic plant used for making cord and baskets

'īlio dog

imu earth oven

'io the Hawaiian hawk

kahiki foreign place or country

kāhili feather standard marking presence of royalty

kahuna priest, minister, expert in any profession

kilapia tilapia

kalo taro

kālua to bake in an underground oven

kanaka, kānaka man, men

kanakalū kangaroo

kāne man, male, husband

Kāne one of the four great Hawaiian gods

kapa tapa, a cloth made from a native plant

kapu forbidden, protected, to restrict

ke the

kiawe mesquite tree, introduced in 1828, common dry-land tree

kīpuka area of vegetation isolated by surrounding lava flow

koa largest of endemic Hawaiian forest trees

ko'a stone or coral fishing shrine

kōlea Pacific golden plover

koloa Hawaiian duck

kopena 'ai 'elelū cockroach wasp

kukui candlenut tree, important culture plant in Hawai'i

kū'ula stone god, site or altar placed near sea to attract fish

lānai patio, deck

lehua red, orange, yellow or white flower of the *ʻōhiʻa* tree

lei garland of flowers, leaves or shells

lepelepe o Hina monarch butterfly

limu seaweed

loʻi, loʻi kalo taro patch

mahalo thank you, gratitude, appreciation

mākāhā sea opening of coastal fishpond, sluice

ma kai seaward, toward the ocean

makika mosquito

mana spiritual or supernatural power

manauea small reddish green edible seaweed, also called by Japanese name *ogo*

manō shark

ma uka inland, toward mountains

moʻo lizard, gecko, dragon

moʻo ʻalā gecko

naonao lele termite

nēnē Hawaiian goose

o of

ʻohana family

ʻōhiʻa lehua native tree; its flower is beloved and its hard wood highly useful

ʻōʻio bonefish

ʻono good, tasty, delicious, yummy

ʻoʻopu wai freshwater goby

pali cliff, precipice

pāpio the young *ulua* or jack; an important food and sport fish

piha full

pili a type of long native grass used to thatch houses; formerly common, now rare

poi starchy food staple made from taro

poloka frog

puaʻa pig

pueo owl

pūpū, pūpū kani oe tree snail

ʻūhini pule praying mantis

Science Glossary

adaptation A trait or character the presence of which enhances survival or reproduction; the process of becoming adapted to a given set of environmental conditions.

adaptive radiation The diversification of a single species or group of related species into new ecological or geographic zones, producing a variety of species.

alien species Any plant or animal that has been intentionally or unintentionally introduced by humans to a given area such as Hawai'i; also referred to as exotic species, introduced species, and nonnative species.

amphibian A class of animals that includes toads, frogs, salamanders and newts. Amphibians are cold-blooded, scaleless vertebrates that begin life in the water, using gills to breathe. In time they develop lungs and are able to live on land.

amphidromous life cycle The cycle of reproduction of several native Hawaiian water species. It begins in fresh water; offspring are then washed *ma kai* and continue to develop while drifting at sea. They later return to fresh water as postlarvae. Native gobies are examples of species with an amphidromous life cycle.

aquaculture The cultivation of plants or animals in water for human consumption. An early form of aquaculture was the very sophisticated use of fishponds by Hawaiians to produce large quantities of fresh fish. Today, *limu* (seaweed), fish and prawns are among the products of aquaculture in Hawai'i. Also called "mariculture."

archipelago A group of neighboring islands stretching across a body of water

arthropod An invertebrate with a segmented body and jointed legs. Spiders, shrimp, centipedes, sowbugs, lobsters and insects are all arthropods.

artificial selection The selective breeding by humans of a plant or animal species to produce a descendant with particular traits. Humans have artificially selected over three hundred different breeds of dogs, all traceable to a common ancestor, the gray wolf.

atoll A low island that consists of a coral reef encircling a submerged volcano and often enclosing a shallow lagoon. Atolls are one of the final stages of erosion as an island is worn back into the ocean.

autotomy The reflex action of certain animals such as the gecko or praying mantis that allows a leg, tail or claw to detach at a break-off point. By discarding the part, the animal may elude capture by a predator or replace a damaged body part. In time a new member will take the place of the discarded one.

avian Of or pertaining to birds. Avian malaria, carried by mosquitoes, is a major threat to endemic Hawaiian birds.

avian malaria A blood disease in birds caused by a parasite. Avian malaria is spread by mosquitoes. It was first reported in Hawai'i in 1947.

avian pox Caused by a virus, this disease is spread by mosquitoes and mites or through contact by infected individuals. Avian pox causes sores on feet, legs and face of the infected bird. First seen in Hawai'i in the early 1890s.

ballast The heavy material placed in a ship hold to give the ship stability. Early sailing ships to Hawai'i often carried as ballast insect-infested earth and rubble, which was then shoveled on shore as the ship was refitted for an outgoing voyage.

biological control The introduction of a natural enemy of a species to reduce or eliminate it. Such natural enemies may include predators, parasites or diseases.

biological diversity The numbers and proportion of different species of plants and animals found in a given area. The area can be as large as an island, a country, or a continent or as small as a *kīpuka* or a cave. A healthy ecosystem usually includes many different species with a rich variety of biological roles and a high rate of genetic variability. Our planet is currently experiencing a sudden and significant decline in the abundance and diversity of organisms, particularly in tropical rain forest areas. The primary cause of this decline is habitat destruction by humans.

biota The animal and plant life of a particular area; the forms of life there

caldera The "bowl" or depression that results from the explosion or collapse of a volcano

camouflage The color or design of an animal's skin that allows it to blend with a natural background. Camouflage makes it hard for a predator to see a prey, or vice versa. Examples of such disguise include the *kōlea* egg, the gecko skin, the sticklike shape and color of the praying mantis and the changing colors of the tilapia.

canopy The upper level of vegetation in a forest, which first receives sunlight. The light is then filtered down to the lower levels of vegetation.

captive propagation The removal of endangered species or their eggs from their natural habitat to assure them a protected area in which to reproduce and hatch and thus increase their numbers. A controlled release back into their habitat is the goal.

carnivorous Flesh-eating. Also used to describe plants such as the Venus flytrap that "eat" insects.

cellulose The main material found in the cell walls or fibers of plants. Cellulose is used to make paper and some types of cloth. It is the food of termites and is also eaten by cockroaches.

chemical control The use of a pesticide to reduce or eliminate a species of animal or plant from a particular area

chorion The membrane surrounding an embryo

chrysalis The case built by a butterfly larva as housing during the pupa stage. The pupa remains in the chrysalis as it prepares for its final butterfly form.

cocoon The case woven by a moth larva. The cocoon provides protection during the pupa stage of development.

coevolution Evolutionary changes in one or more species in response to changes in other species. The shape of the bill of some Hawaiian honeycreepers and the flowers from which they obtained nectar evolved together, the bill and the flower similar in general shape.

colonizer The first plant or animal to occupy an environment not previously inhabited by this species

continental drift A theory suggesting that a supercontinent called Pangaea was split by the forces of tectonic plate shifts to form the present-day continents. Continental drift may help to explain why some animals such as the *honu* and the European eel migrate such vast distances.

decomposer An organism that feeds on organic material in the form of decaying plant or animals. Decomposers are usually the last stage of a food chain.

dengue fever A tropical disease spread by mosquitoes. Symptoms of dengue fever include fever, rash and considerable pain in the joints. Though no cases have been reported in Hawai'i for many years, dengue fever remains a potential threat to humans in Hawai'i.

ecology A branch of biology that studies the relations between living organisms and their environment. Also refers to relations between a specific organism and its environment.

embryo The earliest stage of development of an animal. The embryo is protected by the shell or uterus.

embryonic Of or relating to an embryo

endemic Native only to a specific area and not found anyplace else

estuary The area where the water of a stream or river mixes with seawater

evolution The changes that take place within a line of descent over time that result in modification of a species and the generation of new species

exoskeleton An external skeleton covering the body of an animal such as an insect, snail or crab

exotic Of foreign, not native, origin. In describing a plant or animal species, synonym for "alien."

feral Wild. Often used to describe a domesticated animal that has reverted to a wild state. Feral cats, cattle, horses, goats and sheep have caused severe habitat and species destruction in Hawai'i.

fibropapilloma A disease afflicting turtles, which produces fleshy tumors that frequently lead to death. The cause of this disease is not clearly understood. The epidemic spread of fibropapilloma is of particular concern in the waters of Hawai'i and Florida.

fire-clearing The intentional burning off of vegetation by humans to make available land for agricultural purposes. Fire-clearing is a relatively quick, low-labor technique for clearing land. The burned vegetation provides nutrients to the new crops planted by the farmer. However, fire-clearing also kills most living organisms within the area. It is thought that prehistoric fire-clearing by Hawaiians caused the decrease of many populations of endemic species.

flotation The process by which an animal or plant is carried through the air from one region to another. Many insects and the spores of numerous ferns were carried to Hawai'i in this way. Flotation also refers to seaborne objects.

food chain The flow of food energy through an ecological community as one organism consumes another and in turn is consumed by a "higher" organism. At the "top" of the food chain are organisms with no natural enemies that prey on them. In Hawai'i, microscopic fungi on native plants provide food for endemic tree snails. These snails in turn are consumed by tree rats, which are then themselves hunted by the *'io* (Hawaiian hawk). The *'io* has no natural predator. It is thus at the "top" of the food chain. Food chains can be very complex or quite simple; they commonly begin with a plant and end with a decomposer.

food web A complex transfer of food energy that connects species in different food chains. In the food chain example above, a bird—rather than the rat—might eat the snail, then be eaten by a cat—rather than by the hawk. The bird and cat are part of an "overlapping" food chain.

founder effect The establishment, in a small population that, by chance, leaves a larger one, of genetic traits that differ from those of the original population. Given the very limited genetic variation available in such small populations, certain traits of the founding species are quickly "set" in descendants and show up in notable physical changes in a relatively short time.

gene The basic unit of heredity. The gene contains a hereditary design or code, which is transmitted to a new generation of offspring. The information from numerous genes determines the nature of a species.

habitat The environment of a plant or animal; the area in which it is naturally found

herbivorous Feeding on plants

hermaphroditic Having both male and female reproductive organs

host specific Evolving in a dependent relationship with a particular plant or animal without which the dependent species cannot live

hot spot A weak area in the Earth's crust that allows molten lava, or magma, to well up from the Earth's center

humus The organic part of soil created by the partial decay of plant and animal matter

imprinting Behavior imitation by a young animal of other members of its species, through which it learns response skills to a particular stimulus. In the future, given a similar situation, the animal will respond with the imprinted behavior. Animals in captivity sometimes imprint on humans.

incubation The period in the development of an embryo or egg during which it is maintained by a parent or parents in favorable conditions for hatching or growing

indigenous Native to an area, but also found elsewhere

intentional introduction A plant or animal purposely taken along by humans to provide food, drink, fiber or medicine during a voyage or at the new settlement. Farmers, sportsmen, pet store owners, scientists and others have introduced plants and animals for a variety of reasons. Plants and animals have also been introduced to Hawaiʻi as gifts to residents. Plants and animals brought to Hawaiʻi by the earliest Polynesian voyagers are called Polynesian introductions.

invertebrate An animal that has no backbone or spinal column. Insects and other arthropods are invertebrates, as are worms and mollusks.

joey A young kangaroo or wallaby

kīpuka An area of land consisting of old lava and vegetation surrounded by a newer flow that sometimes lacks vegetation or has very little. The isolated "island," or *kīpuka,* often contains a remarkable variety of unique life forms.

larva A sexually immature stage in various animal groups, often with a form and diet distinct from those of the adult.

leptospirosis A bacterial disease found in streams and freshwater ponds. Leptospirosis is carried in the urine of mice, rats and mongooses and can pass to humans by way of open cuts, the eyes, mouth or nose. This disease is very serious and can cause death in humans. Early symptoms are flu-like: fever, chills, aches, diarrhea and vomiting. See a doctor immediately.

magma Liquid or molten rock from deep within the Earth that wells up and cools as lava

malacologist A scientist who specializes in the study of mollusks

malaria A disease transmitted through the bite of an infected mosquito; it is a common disease in the tropics, but not in Hawai'i. Symptoms of malaria are very severe chills and fevers. See also **avian malaria.**

mantle The semisolid layer of the Earth's interior that lies between the crust and the core

marsupial A group of mammals without a placenta. Instead, the female has a pouch, called a marsupium, on her abdomen, in which the tiny, undeveloped fetus fastens to a teat and spends its first months of life.

metamorphosis The physical change in an animal as it develops to an adult. Change in form, habits and habitat are all part of this developmental process. The mosquito larva, when compared to the adult, looks very different, lives in a different habitat and eats different things. The development of the monarch butterfly from egg to caterpillar, caterpillar to chrysalis and then to adult is another example of metamorphosis.

migration The movement of animals or groups of animals, especially birds and fish, from one geographic area to another, following the change of season or for reproduction

mimicry The imitation by one organism of the color, behavior or form of another organism or object in its environment

mollusk An invertebrate that usually has a shell that covers all or part of its body. The group includes snails and clams, but also octopuses and squids

multiple clutching A technique used by scientists in captive breeding programs; it involves early removal from a nest of a first clutch of eggs. This prompts the female to lay again. The first clutch is hatched by researchers, and the female rears the second one. Multiple clutching increases the year's egg production.

native Occurring naturally in a certain locality; not transported there by humans. Among its native animal species, Hawai'i counts the following: five species of native nonmarine fish, dozens of species of native land birds, and a single land mammal (a bat). Hawai'i has no native amphibians or land reptiles.

natural selection A process, not caused by humans, through which members of a population with the most effective adaptations for coping with environmental pressures will be the most likely to survive and produce offspring. Such adaptations perpetuate desirable genetic traits and eliminate undesirable ones.

niche The physical and biological conditions in which the members of a species live and reproduce.

ornithologist A scientist who specializes in the study of birds.

Pacific Plate The name given to one of a dozen or so huge sections of the Earth's crust called tectonic plates. The Hawaiian Islands are located on the Pacific Plate.

parasitic Obtaining nutrients directly from the tissues of a living host on which it lives and may or may not kill. Living on or in another species for food or protection. Usually the host plant or animal suffers from the relationship.

parthenogenesis Development of an embryo from an unfertilized egg

pigment The materials in cells and tissues that give plants and animals their colors

plate tectonics The movement of the great slabs, or plates, that make up the crust of the Earth. The slow shiftings of these plates cause continental drift, earthquakes and mountain formation.

proboscis The sucking organ of insects such as the butterfly and the mosquito; also, the trunk of an elephant and the snout of animals like the tapir and shrew

protozoan An animal consisting of one cell or a colony of similar cells

pupa An insect in the final developmental stage just before becoming an adult. This is a nonfeeding stage. Often, as in the case of the cockroach wasp or monarch butterfly, the pupa is enclosed in a cocoon or chrysalis.

pupate To enter the pupal stage. In many insects a silken or fibrous case, or cocoon, is spun.

rafting The transport of an animal by flotation from one land mass to another on a drifting log or other debris

regeneration The regrowth of a lost or injured body part such as the tail of a gecko or leg of a praying mantis. Often the new part is slightly stumped.

reptile The class of cold-blooded vertebrates that includes snakes, turtles, lizards, crocodiles and tuatara. Native reptiles in Hawaiian waters include three marine turtles and a poisonous snake.

rookery A breeding place for such animals as turtles, seals and penguins, or birds in general

social insect Insects such as termites, bees or ants that live together in highly complex communities led by a queen. Each member of the community has a specialized role to play, with definite tasks.

spawn The eggs or young produced by fish, amphibians and other water creatures

speciation The splitting of one species into two or more new species.

species A group of interbreeding or potentially interbreeding populations that do not breed with other groups.

spore A one-celled, seedlike organ that can develop into a new individual. Moss, algae and ferns all reproduce by releasing countless spores into the wind or water.

subsistence farming The most simple form of using the land to provide food, clothing and shelter. Subsistence farming involves a minimum use of outside resources not produced by the farm itself.

symbiosis The intimate and permanent dependence on each other of two different species

tectonic plate Geological term for the great pieces or sections of the Earth's crust that make up the surface of our planet. There are a dozen or more large tectonic plates and many smaller ones. The Hawaiian chain is located on the Pacific Tectonic Plate, also called the Pacific Plate.

temperate Not too cold or hot (used to describe climate)

territoriality The often aggressive behavior of an animal as it defends the area in which it feeds or breeds or otherwise sees as its own

territory The area in which an animal population feeds, breeds or nests. Territories are often defended from intruders.

tundra The vast, flat and treeless regions of the arctic parts of North America, Asia and Europe. The *kōlea* (golden plover), flies to the tundra, where it nests. Permafrost, or continuously frozen ground, is characteristic of the tundra, allowing only small plants to grow on the sun-warmed surface.

unintentional introduction Plant or animal that travels to a new location with the help of humans but without their knowledge. Such introductions include stowaways on ships and planes entering our ports and airports.

vertebrate An animal with a spinal column and a brain within a brain case or skull. The vertebrate group includes all mammals, fish, birds, reptiles and amphibians.

Select Bibliography

Balazs, George H. *Recovery Records of Adult Green Turtles Observed or Originally Tagged at French Frigate Shoals, Northwestern Hawaiian Islands.* Springfield, Virginia: National Marine Fisheries Service, 1983.

Baldwin, D.D. *Land and Fresh Water Shells of the Hawaiian Islands.* Honolulu: Press Publishing Co., 1893.

Beckwith, Martha W. *Hawaiian Mythology.* Honolulu: University of Hawai'i Press, 1970.

Behnke, F.L. *A Natural History of Termites.* New York: Charles Scribner's Sons, 1977.

Bell, William J. *The Laboratory Cockroach: Experiments in Cockroach Anatomy, Physiology and Behavior.* New York: Chapman and Hall, 1981.

Bell, William J., and K.G. Adiyodi, eds. *The American Cockroach.* New York: Chapman and Hall, 1982.

Berger, A.J. *Hawaiian Birdlife.* Honolulu: University of Hawai'i Press, 1972.

———. "History of Exotic Birds in Hawai'i." Parts 1 and 2. *'Elepaio* 35(6): 60–65 (1974); 35(7): 72–79 (1975).

Bertram, Brian C.R. *The Ostrich Communal Nesting System.* Princeton, New Jersey: Princeton University Press, 1992.

Brower, Kenneth. "The Pig War." In *A World Between Waves,* ed. by Frank Stewart. Washington, D.C.: Island Press, 1992.

Bryan, E. H., Jr. *Insects We See in Hawaii.* Honolulu: Tongg Publishing Co., 1940.

Bryan, William A. *Natural History of Hawaii.* Honolulu: Gazette Co., 1915.

Carlquist, Sherwin. "The First Arrivals." *Natural History* 91 (12), 1982.

———. *Hawaii: A Natural History.* New York: Natural History Press, 1980.

Carson, Rachel. *The Sense of Wonder.* New York: Harper and Row, 1956.

———. *Under the Sea-Wind.* England: Oxford University Press, 1952.

Caum, Edward L. "The Exotic Birds of Hawaii." Bernice P. Bishop Museum *Occasional Papers.* 10(9, 1933).

Cornwell, P.B. *The Cockroach.* London: Hutchinson Publishing Co., 1968.

Culliney, John L. *Islands in a Far Sea.* San Francisco: Sierra Club Books, 1988.

Daws, Gavan. *Hawaii: The Islands of Life.* Honolulu: Signature Publishing, in association with The Nature Conservancy of Hawai'i, 1988.

Devick, William S. *Patterns of Introductions of Aquatic Organisms to Hawaiian Freshwater Habitats.* Honolulu: Department of Land and Natural Resources, Division of Aquatic Resources, 1991.

Frick, D. "Notes on Hawaiian Terrestrial Conchology." *Sandwich Islands Monthly* 1: 137–140 (1856).

Fullaway, David T., and Noel L.H. Krauss. *Common Insects of Hawai'i.* Honolulu: Krauss Tongg Publishing, 1945.

Gagné, Wayne C. "Conservation Priorities in Hawaiian Natural Systems." *Bioscience* 38(4): 264–271 (1988).

———. "Hawai'i's Tragic Dismemberment." *Defenders* 50 (1975): 461–469.

Giffin, Jon. Ecology of the Feral Pig on the Island of Hawai'i. State of Hawai'i Department of Land and Natural Resources, Division of Fish and Game, Project No. W-15-3, Study No. 11, 68–72.

Gregory, H.E. "The Geography of the Pacific." In *Problems of the Pacific: Proceedings of the Second Conference of the Institute of Pacific Relations*, 221–231. Chicago: University of Chicago Press, 1928.

Hadfield, Michael G. "Extinction in Hawaiian Achatinelline Snails." *Malacologia* 27(1): 67–81 (1986).

Hadfield, Michael G., Stephen E. Miller, and Anne H. Carwile. "The Decimation of Endemic Hawaiian Tree Snails by Alien Predators." *American Zoology* 33 (1993): 610–622.

Handy, E.S. Craighill, and Elizabeth Green Handy. *Native Planters of Hawaii.* Honolulu: Bishop Museum Press, 1972.

Hardy, D.E. *Insects of Hawaii.* Vols. 10–14. Honolulu: University of Hawai'i Press, 1960–81.

Herter, Eric, ed., *Discovery: The Hawaiian Odyssey.* Honolulu: Bishop Museum Press, 1993.

Higa, Stanley Y. "Flight, Colony Foundation and Development of the Gonads of the Primary Reproductives of the Formosan Subterranean Termite, Coptotermes formosanus Shiraki." Ph.D. diss., University of Hawai'i, 1981.

Higa, Stanley Y., and Minoru Tamashiro. *Swarming of the Formosan Subterranean Termite, Coptotermes formosanus Shiraki in Hawaii.* Honolulu: University of Hawai'i Institute of Tropical Agriculture, No. 2778, 1983.

Hōkū o Hawai'i, 1906–48.

Honolulu Advertiser, 1921–.

Honolulu Star-Bulletin, 1912–.

Hosmer, R.S. "The Beginning 5 Decades of Forestry in Hawaii." *Journal of Forestry* 57(2): 27–44 (1959).

Illingworth, J.F. *Early References to Hawaiian Entomology.* Bishop Museum Bulletin 2. Honolulu: Bishop Museum Press, 1923.

Johnson, Edgar. *The Praying Mantis.* New York: Stackpole Sons, 1937.

Kamae, Eddie, and Verna Kamae. *Listen to the Forest.* Hawaii Sons, Inc., 1991. Videotape.

Kamakau, Samuel M. *The Works of the People of Old.* Honolulu: Bishop Museum Press, 1976.

Kay, E. Alison. "Hawaiian Natural History: 1778–1900." In *A Natural History of the Hawaiian Islands: Selected Readings,* ed. E. Alison Kay, 608–653. Honolulu: University of Hawai'i Press, 1972.

Kelly, Marion. *Loko I'a o He'eia: Heeia Fishpond.* Honolulu: Department of Anthropology, Bishop Museum, 1975.

Kepelino, K. *Kepelino's Tradition of Hawai'i.* Edited by Martha W. Beckwith. Bishop Museum Bulletin 95. Honolulu: Bishop Museum Press, 1932.

Kikuchi, W.K. "Prehistoric Hawaiian Fishponds." *Science* 193(4250): 295–299 (1976).

Kirch, Patrick V. "The Impact of the Prehistoric Polynesians on the Hawaiian Ecosystem." *Pacific Science* 36(1): 1–14 (1982).

———. "Transported Landscapes." *Natural History* 91 (12, 1982).

Kramer, Raymond J. *Hawaiian Land Mammals.* Rutland, Vermont: E. Tuttle Co., 1971.

Malo, David. *Hawaiian Antiquities.* Honolulu: Bishop Museum Press, 1951.

Meyen, F.J.F. Chapter 12 of "Reise um de Erde...1830–1832." Vol. 2. Translated by W.D. Alexander. Manuscript, Bishop Museum Library, Honolulu.

Menzies, Archibald. *Hawai'i Nei 128 Years Ago.* Edited by W.F. Wilson. Honolulu, 1920.

Montgomery, S.L. "Carnivorous Caterpillars: The Behavior, Biogeography and Conservation of *Eupithecia* (Lepidoptera: Geometridae) in the Hawaiian Islands." *Geojournal* 7(1982): 549–556.

Morris, Desmond. *Mammal Watching*. New York: Crown Publishing, 1990.

Munro, G.C. *Birds of Hawaii.* Bridgeway Press, 1960.

Munro, G.C. *Birds of Hawaii.* Rutland, Vermont: Charles E. Tuttle Co., Inc., 1967.

Nishida, Gordon M., and Joann M. Tenorio. *What Bit Me? Identifying Hawai'i's Stinging and Biting Insects and Their Kin.* Honolulu: University of Hawai'i Press, 1993.

———. *What's Bugging Me? Identifying and Controlling Household Pests in Hawai'i.* Honolulu: University of Hawai'i Press, 1995.

Nūpepa Kū'oko'a, 1861–1929.

Paradise of the Pacific: Hawaii's Illustrated Monthly Magazine, 1888–1966.

Perkins, R.C.L. Introduction to *Fauna Hawaiiensis.* Edited by David Sharp. Cambridge: Cambridge University Press, 1913.

Pilsbry, Henry A., and C. Montague Cooke, Jr. *Notes on Hawaiian Land Shells.* Honolulu: Bishop Museum Press, 1908.

Pratt, H.D., P.L. Bruner, and D.G. Berret. *A Field Guide to the Birds of Hawaii and the Tropical Pacific.* Princeton, New Jersey: Princeton University Press, 1987.

Pukui, Mary Kawena. *'Ōlelo No'eau: Hawaiian Proverbs and Poetic Sayings.* Honolulu: Bishop Museum Press, 1983.

Pukui, Mary Kawena, and Samuel H. Elbert. *Hawaiian Dictionary.* Honolulu: University of Hawai'i Press, 1986.

Rock, J.F. *The Indigenous Trees of the Hawaiian Islands.* Honolulu, 1913.

Rosenblatt, L.M. *Monarch Magic.* Charlotte, Vermont: Williamson Publishing Co., 1998.

Ross, E.S. "Mantids: The Praying Predators." *National Geographic* 165 (February 1984).

Stivens, Dal. *The Incredible Egg: A Billion Year Journey.* New York: Weybright and Talley, 1974.

Stone, C.P., and B.S. Stone, eds. *Conservation Biology in Hawai'i.* Honolulu Cooperative National Resources Studies Unit, University of Hawai'i, Mānoa, 1989.

Summers, C.C. *Hawaiian Fishponds.* Honolulu: Bishop Museum Special Publications, Bishop Museum Press, 1964.

Pacific Commercial Advertiser, 1856–1921

Polynesian, 1840–44.

Sales Builder, 1932–1941.

Tinker, Spencer W. *Animals of Hawaii: A Natural History of the Amphibians, Reptiles, and Mammals Living in the Hawaiian Islands.* Honolulu: Nippu Jiji, 1938.

Titcomb, Margaret. *Dog and Man in the Ancient Pacific, with Special Attention to Hawaii.* Honolulu: Star-Bulletin Printing Co., 1969.

Tomich, P. Quentin. *Mammals in Hawaii.* Honolulu: Bishop Museum Press, 1886.

Zimmerman, E.C. *Insects of Hawaii.* Honolulu: University of Hawai'i Press, 1948.

INDEX

Page numbers in bold type refer to photographs.

I

J

K

L

M

N

O

P

R

S